Contents

WITHIN THESE FOUR WALLS

A local housegroup
share their problems

by Mary Batchelor

Illustrated by Nick Butterworth

SCRIPTURE UNION
5 Wigmore Street, London, W.1

By the same author:
ALL FOR GOOD
WINTER'S ROOTS
YOUR TEENAGERS

© 1969 Mary Batchelor
First published 1969

SBN 85421 210 8

Printed by A. McLay & Co. Ltd. Cardiff and London

Chapter 1
MEET THE GROUP

THE following chapters give some account of discussions between a group of Christians on matters of everyday concern.

Wendon is a village just off a main North to South road, about three miles distant from the medium-sized market town of Fairwell. It is a village that combines the old with new development, and retains its charm and beauty in spite of its nearness to the industries of Northern England.

The members of the group live near each other and meet at regular intervals for prayer and Bible study. The group consists of:

Jack Thomas—a bank manager in Fairwell, aged about forty-five, in whose home the group meets.

Brenda Thomas—his wife—also in her forties, pretty, tending to plumpness; has an only daughter of eighteen.

Dennis Carter Brown—chemical engineer, aged twenty-eight; leader of the church youth club.

Sheila Carter Brown—his wife, aged twenty-seven; thin and auburn-haired; a science graduate of the red-brick university where she met her husband; has two small children—girl and boy.

Fred Peters—in his late fifties; formerly a chargehand with Brit-Chem, but since industrial accident, runs a flourishing general store on a new housing estate.

Miriam Peters—his wife; in her mid-fifties; comfortably built, fair-haired; has five children, four now married; one much younger son (John) thirteen, still at home.

Eileen Gordon—about twenty-six, unmarried, one of a large family; left school at earliest opportunity and is now a typist with International Steel Co.; dark, with glasses.

* * * * * *

Brenda Thomas stooped to straighten a rug, tidy the *Radio Times* and some magazines; she then crossed the room to check her reflection in the mirror. Her eyes strayed from her own face to the reflected image of her husband, stretched out in his favourite chair and absorbed in the paper.

'You know they'll be arriving any minute, Jack?' she asked, aware that he was perfectly prepared for the evening, and, unlike her, delightfully able to deal with each moment as it came. He nodded, smiled back at her in the mirror, and turned the page. Brenda went out to the kitchen, which gleamed with cleanness and modern, streamlined efficiency, and began to set out cups and saucers on a tray. She loved her home, with its perfect combination of age and contemporary comfort. She had a flair for home-making and for creating beauty and order, combined with comfort. Life might have been different if they had had a large family, but their only daughter, Rosemary, was neither noisy nor careless, and the restful pattern of their life was preserved.

Meanwhile, in one of the labour-saving, space-saving, architect-designed houses off School Lane, the Carter Browns were getting ready for the evening out. Sheila raced up the stairs to have a last look at the children, shouting down to Dennis to show the new baby-sitter how the radiogram worked.

She gave a despairing glance at the bathroom, with its pile of towels and small, grubby garments, and scattered fleet of rubber ducks, then closed the door firmly. For once the children had fallen asleep early and she tiptoed out of their bedroom before hurrying into her own for shoes, coat and a quick smarten up. She had never found much leisure to look after her own appearance and, as she hastily put a comb through her hair, she imagined Brenda Thomas looking relaxed and well-groomed when they arrived at her house. Remembering suddenly that she had provided no refreshments for the 'sitter', she flew downstairs without another thought for herself to find the jar of instant coffee and a packet of biscuits.

Dennis had finished, and much enjoyed, giving details of the possible performance of his radiogram, and was waiting, slightly impatiently, for his wife to come.

'Now we'll have to take the car or be late, I suppose,' he remarked, when she reappeared from the kitchen, and he made his way to the garage.

'Sorry there's no telly,' Sheila paused to say apologetically, 'it's all hi-fi and stereo with Dennis at the moment, but he'll come down to earth once the children are a bit older.'

'You ready, Dad?' Mrs. Peters asked, her nylon fur hat settled comfortably on her head, and her tweed coat buttoned up.

'Yes, the shop's properly locked up and I've seen to the side door too. Will John be out all evening?'

'He's round at Reg Jackson's and says he won't be home till after us. But I don't want to be late back.'

They set off down the road, giving a last glance

back at their corner shop to see that all was well before turning first into Laburnum Avenue and then into the main Fairwell Road.

'It looks like Eileen in front there,' Mr. Peters remarked, 'but we can't catch her up. Yes, she's crossing over to School Lane, she'll be there before us tonight.'

Eileen Gordon, hurrying ahead, was glad to be alone. There were always so many people around, at home and at work. She even had to share a bedroom with a younger sister. Being alone was almost a luxury, with its opportunity to think about the things that pleased or annoyed her, the problems that teased her mind and demanded to be solved. She wondered if other people chewed and worried at the situations of life as much as she did, and with as little result. Ahead of her the outline of the church came into view and the semi-circle of houses around the Green. From the far side a porch light gleamed and she hurried across the grass to reach the warmth of the house ahead.

Ten minutes later they were all there, ready to begin, perched or relaxed in their chairs, according to temperament, in Brenda and Jack Thomas's sitting-room.

'Any suggestions as to what we should study next?' Jack asked.

Eileen spoke quickly, before Mr. Peters could suggest, as she suspected he might, Leviticus or the Book of Revelation.

'Could we do something a bit different this session? I'd like to be able to discuss some of the everyday problems we come across, and the Christian way of solving them.'

'What does everyone else think?' Jack asked.

'It's a good idea,' Sheila said at once. 'I've always got hundreds of things I want to sort out. In fact, something cropped up this morning which I've been worrying over all day, getting tied up in knots on my own.'

'Come on, then, let's be having it,' Dennis said.

So they began.

Chapter 2

PEOPLE MATTER MORE THAN MEETINGS

'I WAS just nipping out to the dust-bin this morning, when Mrs. Johnson gave a call. She lives in the bungalow at the back of us. You probably know her by sight. She's often around in the village and she always has a scruffy white poodle with her. She was hanging out the washing, so I went across to the fence. She asked if I'd missed her lately, which was a bit awkward because, until then, I hadn't noticed that she'd not been about. Apparently she's had 'flu and today is the first time she's been out of the house. Her husband is never very well—he has bronchitis badly—and she's really been stuck, with no one to get in the shopping or take the precious poodle out. He was her chief concern of course. By the time she'd told me the whole story, I felt quite guilty, specially as she still didn't look any too fit. Mind you, I wasn't to know she was ill, and I told her she should have got her husband to call and ask me to help. Then what do you think she said? "I knew you'd be too busy with your church work." I felt awful—and it was a shock to think people feel like that about us.

'I said something about never being too busy to help a neighbour, but it made me think. Is that really how people see us? Like the priest and the Levite in the parable of the Good Samaritan? Too busy being religious to show a bit of kindness to someone in need? I decided that at least I could go across later and get her washing in and iron it for her. It didn't take long—it was a good dry this morning—and when I took the clothes back all done, she seemed really pleased. But then she insisted on making tea and keeping me talking for ages, and I felt fed up. I'd hoped to get the children in bed early, as we were coming out tonight, and I'd work to get on with at home. I'd hoped to get all the invitations to the Young Wives' Group put in envelopes and addressed, and my visual aid prepared for the Bible Class on Sunday. It's the afternoon the children go to Pat's, up the road, and I like to get those sort of jobs done while they're out of the way. I'm honestly ready to help a neighbour, but I can't afford to waste time.'

'Was it wasted time?' Brenda asked. 'I would have thought it did you good to sit and relax sometimes, anyway.'

'But I wasn't relaxed,' Sheila insisted, 'and it wasn't even useful talk. I'm not interested in what the dog likes for its dinner, or what other people's sister's children had for Christmas.'

'Well, I do think you're stuck up,' Eileen exclaimed, 'and just thinking about yourself. I'm sorry, I suppose that sounded rude.'

'It did,' Sheila agreed, and then laughed. 'It's no good getting huffy about *your* comments, Eileen. Come on, explain what you mean.'

'Well, I know you're very intellectual and high-brow, but most of us aren't, and I don't think it's very nice to be high and mighty about what ordinary people are interested in. Being stuck up about your brain-power is just as bad as being a snob because you're rich or upper-class.'

'I don't think your time *was* wasted as far as Mrs. Johnson goes,' Mrs. Peters said. 'I expect it was as good as a tonic to her to talk to someone, after being shut up in the house for a week or two. Hasn't she any family of her own?'

'No, but she's one of these people who's mad about children. I had to look at all the photos of her great-nieces and nephews in Canada. She kept saying she wished I'd bring our children round to see her.'

'She doesn't know what she's asking for,' Dennis remarked darkly.

'I think I have been intolerant,' Sheila admitted. 'I mean, the way I moaned about her small-talk. It isn't really just that I feel above it, Eileen, it's more a matter of time. I've taken on all kinds of jobs at church—the kind of things I'm really cut out for—organizing and teaching and so on. If I do these jobs efficiently, how am I to find time for being neighbourly?'

'Perhaps you may have just a bit too much on at church,' Mrs. Peters suggested, 'at least, while the children are tiny. It's easy to be too busy with meetings and church work, so that we've no time for people.'

'I think we've become slaves to more and more meetings,' Brenda agreed; 'you can be so busy doing organized Christian things that you haven't the time or strength to be a normal, understanding human being. I'd like to scrap the whole timetable of weekly activities at church for a bit, and use the time to become relaxed and human—and a good neighbour.'

'It's a matter of getting our priorities right,' Jack said, 'and not going to one extreme or the other. Relationships matter a lot, and although youth work and women's groups and so on are important, they ought not to engross so much of us that we can't give ourselves—our whole attention and time—to people.'

'But I like to see results for the time and energy I use,' Sheila complained.

'Getting to know someone is often a long business,' Mrs. Peters agreed, 'and it doesn't always look as if you're getting anywhere. But you gain a lot as well as giving a lot if you give yourself to people without grudging. Mind, I understand how you feel. I used to fret about the time when mine were little. I didn't do all the work at church that you do, Mrs. Brown, but my days were pretty full. Then someone would call and my plans for the day would all go astray because they wanted a sit-down and a cup of tea and a bit of a chat. I used to get very irritable inwardly, you know, till one day I was reading in the Gospels, and it came to me that the Lord had days like that. Nothing but interruptions, He had, but He welcomed them all and never made anyone feel unwelcome, or as if they ought to be quick with what they had to say and then hurry off. He let His Father plan the days for Him, I think, and I've tried since to do the same. It's a funny thing, but if you welcome the interruptions and kind of accept the changes in plan, they don't seem half the trouble. Mind, I'd often think of something I could do as I talked—a bit of mending or ironing. You could ask Mrs. Johnson to your place, and she'd most likely keep an eye on the children, or help you address envelopes, and feel cheered that she'd been of use.'

'You mean I could work-study Mrs. Johnson to some extent?' Sheila asked, smiling. 'It would make me more relaxed and ready to listen to her.'

'My objection to Mrs. Johnson and her kind is that they aren't really people in need,' Dennis said. 'I think, as Christians, we should be relieving the real social evils of the world. We should be in the forefront, helping to organize food supplies for the underfed and rehousing the homeless. Some of our work at church is concerned with the under-privileged, and I still think Sheila's better employed organizing that than nattering to the well-fed, neurotic types who live round here.'

'There you are,' Eileen said triumphantly, 'you said "neurotic". That shows that Mrs. Johnson and her sort have got needs. You can need help badly without being hungry or homeless.'

'I think it can be easier to help people who live in other countries or who have a different background from our own,' Brenda observed. 'We ought not to run away from our own set. I think Eileen's right—just because they haven't material needs doesn't mean they don't need us. It's fine to run youth clubs for the East Street families, and take them parcels of old clothes, but God has put us in a particular place, and we ought to help meet the needs of our own group and mix in a bit. It's often harder, because being with your own class of people can make you feel a fish out of water. I'm much more self-confident when I speak at the Mothers' Meeting at the Dock Mission than when I go to a dinner with some of Jack's colleagues and their wives. I'm suddenly aware that because I'm a Christian I haven't the time or interest to do the things that fill their lives. But I still don't think I should opt out of my own natural setting.'

'You should be preaching the Gospel to them,' Mr. Peters said; 'we've had a lot of talk about good works, but our job is to preach.'

'Look, it's love your neighbour, not preach at him,' Dennis said hotly.

'Yes, love his immortal soul,' Mr. Peters insisted.

'But not treat him as if he's all soul and nothing else,' Dennis went on. 'It's a fat lot of good preaching the Gospel to someone who's cold or hungry. We must relieve social conditions first.'

'But we ought to be trying to convert people, oughtn't we?' Eileen asked, dubiously. 'I don't mean we ought to preach at them, or hand out tracts, but shouldn't we say something to them about being a Christian? I do agree with Dennis about giving them food and all that kind of thing, but is that enough?'

'Our Lord saw people as a whole, and dealt with

17

all their needs,' Jack said. 'He healed them, fed them when they were hungry, discussed their problems *and* preached the good news of the Gospel. He dealt with every level of need. He knew what doctors and psychiatrists are beginning to find out, that as human beings we need treating as a whole person. Our health can be affected as well as our nerves when we're depressed or feel a sense of guilt.'

'Well, I'm all right at being friendly and giving a helping hand,' Eileen said; 'they all come to me at work if they can't sort out their knitting patterns or their boy-friends let them down, but I just don't seem much good at helping what Mr. Peters calls their immortal souls. I seem to get tongue-tied when I try to talk about my faith.'

'You can always quote the Scriptures to them,' Mr. Peters advised.

'I don't suppose that would make much more sense than someone quoting Shakespeare would to me,' Eileen put in.

'There are modern translations of the New Testament,' Dennis suggested, 'several of them in paperback form. Most people talk about what they think the Bible teaches, but if you ask them point blank whether they've read it, they usually admit they haven't. Then's your opportunity to lend them a copy—I usually keep one or two handy for the purpose—and suggest they read it as they would an ordinary paperback. When they see that it isn't all old-fashioned words and tiny print on wafer-thin paper, they're usually prepared to have a go. I'm sure that does them a lot more good than hearing unconnected snippets and texts quoted at them.'

'I agree about that,' Brenda said, 'but if we try to

18

explain our faith in out-of-date phrases and words that don't mean a thing to non-believers, we shan't be able to follow up their interest. You still hear people trotting out things like "being saved from your sins", not to mention words like "justification" and so on, which may mean a lot to them but leave everyone else mystified.'

'There are bound to be some technical terms in theology, just as there are in everything else,' Sheila said, 'but we still ought to know what they mean well enough to explain them in non-technical terms to other people. It's no good trotting out clichés, either, to describe what happened when we were converted. They just don't ring true, somehow.'

'You've hit the nail on the head when you talk about not ringing true', Eileen agreed, 'I think I used to be like that—you know, talking as if I'd never had a worry since I trusted Jesus. Then I began to see that it just wouldn't wash, saying that sort of thing to the people at home or at work who saw me in a beastly mood or worried stiff about something. I still sing "Christ is the answer to my every need", and I believe it can be so, but at least I know I haven't worked it out properly yet. I must think out the right words to explain my faith, but if that's going to mean anything, I must make my faith work, so that my neighbours see what Christ means to me.'

'I suppose if we're really to succeed in keeping the second commandment—to love our neighbour—we've to put the first and greatest commandment into practice, and love God with all our heart and strength,' Jack said. 'When we're right with Him, we're likely to do right by our neighbour.'

SOME QUESTIONS TO THINK ABOUT

Who is my neighbour?

Am I so busy with church activity that I have no time to give to my neighbour?

Is my timetable so rigid that I have no time for people?

Do I show love for my neighbour at every level of his need?

Have I made the Christian faith my own—in the way I explain it and put it into practice?

Do I fight shy of living the Christian life and talking about the Christian faith among those of my own 'set'?

Does God really come first in my affections?

SOME VERSES TO HELP

"Master, which is the greatest commandment in the Law?" He answered, "Love the Lord your God with all your heart, with all your soul, with all your mind." That is the greatest commandment. It comes first. The second is like it: "Love your neighbour as yourself" (Matt. 22. 36-38, NEB).

"Which of these three seems to you to have been a neighbour . . . ?"

"The man who gave him practical sympathy."

"Then you go and give the same," returned Jesus. (The whole story is found in Luke 10. 29–37).

"Let your light so shine before men, that they may see your good works and give glory to your Father who is in Heaven" (Matt. 5. 16, RSV).

"Be ready at any time to give a quiet and reverent answer to any man who wants a reason for the hope that you have within you" (1 Pet. 3. 15, Phillips).

"His orders are that we should put our trust in the name of His Son, Jesus Christ, and love one another" (1 John 3. 23, Phillips).

"My children, love must not be a matter of words or talk; it must be genuine, and show itself in action" (1 John 3. 18, NEB).

Chapter 3

KITCHEN SINKS ARE ALL RIGHT FOR CABBAGES

EVEN before they had begun that evening it was plain to see that Mr. Peters was on the war-path. He cleared his throat with determination the moment the preliminary buzz of conversation had died down and, opening his large Bible, read out:

'That they may teach the young women to be sober, to love their husbands, to love their children, to be discreet, chaste, keepers at home, good, obedient to their own husbands, that the word of God be not blasphemed (Titus 2, verses 4 and 5).'

He closed his Bible, looked searchingly round the room and repeated with emphasis ' "keepers at home" '.

Sheila Carter Brown sat very upright in her chair, a slow wave of colour spreading up her neck and into her face. Looking across at her, Eileen decided that she was more angry than embarrassed.

Jack Thomas said as lightly and pleasantly as he could, 'Are you referring to some problem for us to discuss, Mr. Peters?'

'It isn't a problem at all as far as I can see it, but a matter on which the Word of God speaks clearly. As you've all heard, the command is for married women to stay at home. I've told that already to our friend Mrs. Brown, but I feel led to make the matter clear to this whole company.'

'The phrase you've quoted—"keepers at home"— doesn't even occur in the RSV,' Sheila objected.

'The Authorized Version has been good enough for past generations of God's people, and it's good enough for me,' Mr. Peters insisted.

'It's not really a matter of whether it's good enough but whether it gives the correct meaning,' Sheila objected. 'After all, even the same words have come to mean something different now from what they meant when the AV was translated. From what I can find out, the phrase means domestic, but certainly not tied to the kitchen sink the whole while.'

'Now wait a moment, you two,' Dennis said, 'you don't seem to realize that everyone else is still in the dark as to what you're talking about. They've probably grasped the fact that you hold different views.'

'Yes, on the subject of working wives,' Sheila

interrupted. 'You see, I've been thinking of getting back to teaching, so I took round a notice to go in Mr. Peter's shop window advertising for a reliable mother's help. When Mr. Peters found out what I intended doing he told me his view that it was wrong for me to go out to work. I don't follow his argument.'

'I believe that the Scriptures make it plain,' Mr. Peters reiterated.

'Well, as I was saying just now,' Sheila went on, I've looked up that passage from Titus that you've been quoting, and it doesn't seem to mean "keepers at home" as much as "home-lovers", or "workers at home". I don't see that I shall stop working at home just because I choose to work somewhere else for a few hours each day. I'll probably love my home more, not less, because I escape from the drudgery for a bit.'

'Of course there wouldn't have been any career wives in St. Paul's day anyway,' Dennis said, 'but he must have been trying to correct some wrong tendency when he gave those instructions to first-century Christian wives.'

Sheila looked across at him as if she was wondering which side he was really on.

'Yes, we do need to think about the principle behind the instruction,' Jack agreed. 'Circumstances are so different for women today that we need to work out how the verse applies to our twentieth-century society. St. Paul certainly seems to be emphasizing . . . '

'That a woman's place is in the home,' Mr. Peters interrupted.

'That's just Victorian, not Christian,' Sheila retorted.

'As I was just saying,' Jack interposed, 'a woman's best opportunity to show her Christian faith in action is within her own home. A Christian wife and mother can provide the right environment for her husband and children, and as well as that her home can be a centre of peace and help for a wide circle of people all around. The home is the natural setting for her. She's got a Christian job to do there, according to St. Paul.'

'In other words, you too are against wives going out to work?' Sheila asked.

Jack smiled. 'Relax! I'm not particularly for or against, but just explaining what seems to be the most important work for Christian wives.'

'You mean that provided I made sure I was doing my main job well—as a wife and mother—it would be all right to have a career as well?' Sheila asked.

'Don't ask me—ask yourself. You've to answer the question of whether it's possible to do both things well.'

'If you ask me, you married women want to have your cake and eat it,' Eileen grumbled. 'Give me an ever-loving husband and a couple of kids and I'd never ask to darken the office door again.'

'That's what you think now,' Sheila said ominously, 'but you should see how you feel after a few years of washing nappies and peeling spuds. I sometimes feel my brain rotting away—it's quite frightening.'

'Well, I haven't got much there to rot,' Brenda said, with a laugh, 'but I do remember feeling more than usually like a cabbage when Rosemary was tiny. I can only say that the worst stage doesn't last long, and surprisingly soon you find time to think straight again. By the time Rosemary started school I found that I'd got lazy—mentally, I mean—so I took myself in hand by listening to schools broadcasts and going to an afternoon class on flower arrangement. I must say, once I made an effort I found I'd even improved with keeping during the years when my mind had been idle.'

'That's very comforting,' Sheila said, 'but I'm sometimes afraid I'll go potty before our children get to the school stage.'

Mr. Peters cleared his throat to speak and Brenda decided it was necessary to say what had been on her mind from the beginning.

'I really don't mean to be personal, Mr. Peters, but have you considered that Mrs. Peters is a working wife?'

'Well, the shop is on the home premises,' Mr. Peters countered.

'I don't really think that alters things,' Brenda said gently, 'and I don't mean it in the least as a criticism of you, Mrs. Peters. In fact I'm just trying to show that it can be done.'

Mr. Peters was temporarily silenced, and after a little pause Sheila asked, 'Well, does anyone else think there are any further considerations for a would-be working wife to take into account?'

'I think a lot depends on your health,' Eileen said. 'A girl in our office is married with one toddler and a baby, and, honestly, she's always in a shocking state—complaining about headaches and tiredness and I don't know what. She's usually late in the morning because she's had to take the child to the nursery and the baby to her mother's. She spends her lunch-hour shopping, then packs up a quarter of an hour early so as to be ready to dash off the moment it's five o'clock. I don't think she's being fair to anybody.'

'Temperament comes into it as well as physical toughness,' Jack said, 'I've seen it with our staff. Some of the married ones don't seem to worry or fuss, while for others the divided loyalties of home and work involve too much personal strain.'

'Of course, Sheila isn't thinking of full-time work just yet,' Dennis said, 'but even so, some jobs are more demanding than others. Teaching may be ideal from the point of view of the hours away from home, but, like medicine or social work, it demands a great deal of the person. I wonder how much emotional energy and interest or patience would be left over for the family?'

Sheila shot another penetrating look at her husband.

'I tried it once,' Brenda announced, 'taking a job, I mean. It was before we moved here and after Rosemary had been at school for a year or two. I worked part-time in a solicitor's office. It wasn't any of the things that have been mentioned that decided me to give it up. I felt I should because I found I was having no time for any sort of Christian work. At least, I still kept on my Sunday School class, but it wasn't easy to spare an evening for the preparation class or for the mid-week children's activity I'd been helping to run. I didn't feel like having folk in at weekends either, and I never seemed to be at home when people called, needing to chat over their problems or their plans. I decided my job would have to go—though I missed the pin-money, of course.'

'Yes, the money,' Sheila said bitterly; 'that's all people seem to think you're doing it for. These days, by the time we have paid for help at home, laundry and more expensive quick foods, I'll not be much in pocket. I'm not thinking of the money.'

'Very high-minded,' Jack said with a smile, 'then how would you sum up your basic reason for wanting to go back to work?'

'I suppose the need to fulfil myself—use every part of myself to the full,' Sheila said.

'I don't think that's such a lofty reason as it sounds at first,' Eileen commented. 'It could be just selfishness on your part. After all, I often feel the need of a husband and children in order to fulfil myself, but I don't make an all-out effort to get married at any price. If you've chosen to fulfil your instincts as a woman I think you ought to consider the people who depend on you now—your husband and family. I bet they won't be properly fulfilled if you're teaching.'

Sheila laughed in spite of herself.

'Do you think I'd be depriving my family, Jack?' she asked.

'Most experts these days seem to agree that pre-school children need their mother most of the time. So if you can afford to stay at home with them while they're tiny, I think, as a Christian, you should do so, and not fall below the standards of motherhood which non-Christians set.'

'It's very nice to be a man and be able to pontificate on wifely duties,' Sheila remarked, 'but when you're the person involved it's not very easy to be so highminded or even be sure how to know whether you're doing the right thing.'

Mrs. Peters spoke for the first time.

'I'll tell you what I've always gone by, dear,' she

said, 'making sure I'm in the place where the Lord wants me.'

'And how am I to know where that is?' Sheila asked impatiently.

'It's not always easy, but if you really want to know the Lord's will and not just to please yourself, it's my experience that He'll make it clear. First of all, as we've said, since you've been given children, you know you've a duty to them and to your husband. They need you a lot while they're so tiny, and children sense when you're always rushing and too busy to give them your full attention. They learn to talk to you and tell you their troubles right from the start, and if you've not time to listen when they're young, then I can't believe they'll come and confide in you when they're bigger. Then, as Mrs. Thomas said, you've got your Christian work too—your youth work and the Young Wives, as well as the neighbourhood visiting. It wouldn't seem right for them to have to go. I think the Lord uses such things to point the way. If you still felt He wanted you back teaching, too, then I believe He'd make it clear by opening up the way, and He'd give you the conviction that you were doing right and not just pleasing yourself.'

'I think it's important for your husband to be in full agreement about your going back to work,' Brenda suggested. 'It's bound to affect him too, and he'll need to do extra to help in the house, probably.'

'Maybe it sounds old-fashioned,' Mrs. Peters said, 'but I've always believed in doing what my husband wants.'

'That's scriptural, not old-fashioned,' Mr. Peters said.

'Well, there certainly are a good many verses about obeying your husband,' Mrs. Peters agreed.

'Phillips translates it "adapt yourself",' Sheila said, on the defensive again.

'That's a good way of putting it,' Mrs. Peters agreed. 'It's a funny sort of household where father and family have to fit in with the mother's wishes and hours of work, instead of the other way round. You'll find your two grow up quick enough, dear, and you'll have time for teaching when that time comes. Meanwhile, there's nothing quite like the peace and satisfaction that come from knowing you're in the place of the Lord's choosing.'

* * * * * *

'I don't understand, Dennis,' Sheila said, as she closed the door after the baby-sitter, and sauntered out to the kitchen. 'I thought you felt as strongly as I do about women wasting their brains standing at a kitchen sink. You always used to say that a woman has as much right to a career as her husband. That was before we were married, I know, and of course I expected to have a year or two at home, having the the family. But you've been very silent the last few weeks since I broached the subject again, and tonight I almost felt you were on the side of Mr. Peters and his followers. When it comes to the push, most men are dying to say "a woman's place is in the home".'

'I haven't said it,' Dennis said guardedly.

'But it's how you feel, isn't it?'

'Well, all right, for the moment I suppose it is. Honestly, I don't want to fence you in, and I *do* still think that women like you should have a career, but when it comes to it, I feel that the kids need you at home a bit longer—in fact we all do. It won't be long before they're at school, and that will be different.'

'If that's the way you see it,' Sheila said, 'I'll do no more about getting a job. This is something we've got to be a hundred per cent agreed on. Just at this moment I could howl—I suppose it's the accumulated effect of the whole evening—and yet, I've a funny sort of feeling that it's the right decision to wait a bit. It's nothing to do with Mr. Peters or St. Paul, but just that I want us to be in agreement in all we do—and I really do take notice of what you say—when I can see some sense in it.'

SOME QUESTIONS TO THINK ABOUT

If a wife does not go out to work, in what other ways can she prevent her mind from stagnating?

If I am a wife, have I accepted fully the rôle of home-maker?

Is our home a centre of Christian help and influence for the family and any who come to it?

Have we, as husband and wife, reached full agreement about both working outside the home?

Will our Christian work suffer if we are both employed?

Will our children suffer if they are looked after by others?

Are we willing to follow God's will in the arranging of time and using of gifts?

SOME VERSES TO HELP

The old women . . . should be examples of the good life, so that the younger women may learn to love their husbands and their children, to be sensible and chaste, home-lovers, kind-hearted and willing to adapt themselves to their husbands—a good advertisement for the Christian faith (Titus 2. 4, 5, Phillips). Whatever you do, put your whole heart and soul into it, as into work done for the Lord (Col. 3. 23, Phillips).

I implore you by God's mercy to offer your very selves to Him: a living sacrifice, dedicated and fit for His acceptance, the worship offered by mind and heart.

Adapt yourselves no longer to the pattern of this present world, but let your minds be remade and your whole nature thus transformed. Then you will be able to discern the will of God, and to know what is good, acceptable and perfect (Rom. 12. 1, 2, NEB).

Chapter 4

YOU'RE NEVER IN, DAD; YOU'RE ALWAYS AT THE CHURCH

'SHEILA not coming tonight?' Brenda asked, as Dennis arrived, late and full of apologies.

'Well, actually, we've got my mother staying and the children are a bit off colour at the moment.'

'Poor Sheila! Didn't she need you at home to help?'

'Don't say that! I was only too glad to get out of the house.'

Brenda said nothing and there was a short silence. Then Dennis went on: 'Actually, I told Sheila I might discuss the whole matter with you tonight and get your views. I know it may not seem the thing to talk about our domestic problems, but we came to the conclusion that there must be crowds of others in the same boat. May I carry on and explain, or is there anything else on the agenda?'

'Nothing that won't keep,' Jack assured him, 'so fire ahead.'

'Last night was a bit of an all-timer, and I think it brought to a head all sorts of feelings and resentments that had been there, deep down, for some time. To start with, I had one of those days at work— a spot of trouble with a new process—so I got home late, hoping to find a meal all ready to eat before dashing off to the Youth Club. I'll admit I'd forgotten that my mother was due to arrive this morning and that Sheila would probably be having her usual pre-mother-in-law cleaning spree. Actually, it was pure chaos—both kids had chosen that day to be ill and had been sick over nearly everything that Sheila had got round to washing or cleaning. I managed to scrounge a bit of cold meat and then I had to get off to the club.

'It was when I got home that we had the whole thing out. I won't give you a ball-by-ball commentary of proceedings, but you can imagine the sort of things we said in the state we were both in by then. Mind you, I can see Sheila's point of view and in one way I'd have liked to stay at home for the evening and help—it was my mother, after all, who was coming— but I honestly felt that it was my duty to go to the club. While we were on the subject of my leaving her,

34

Sheila mentioned the fact that I'm out almost every evening, which I am. Now that we have the new hut for the club, I'm down there Mondays and Wednesdays, and I've been helping the lads to decorate it, and so on, on Saturday afternoons too. Sunday and Tuesday nights I'm at church, some Thursdays we're here and on Fridays I have my night school lecture at Southborough. Saturday morning is free usually, and Saturday night, but I suppose that's not much. Sheila feels I'm not doing my duty as a father and that she and the children will suffer. I can see her point, but I honestly believe that I should put God's work first.'

'When our youngsters were little,' Mr. Peters said, 'I was out every night on the Lord's work and I left them to the Lord to care for.'

'Go on, Mr. Peters,' Eileen said, 'I bet it was Mrs. Peters you left them to, really.'

'She was a wonderful mother,' Mr. Peters stated, refusing to be drawn into argument. 'It's your place to do God's work, Mr. Brown,' he assured Dennis.

'That's what I've rather felt, and I've read of missionaries and Christian leaders who have given up everything for God, and trusted to Him to care for their families.'

'Yes, and look how missionaries' children sometimes turn out!' Jack said.

'But doesn't it say in the Gospels that we should hate wife and children for Christ's sake?' Dennis persisted.

'That means, of course, that Christ must come first in our loyalty and affection, and that we must think of pleasing Him before pleasing them. I suppose if we had times of persecution, like some Christians

35

are going through today, we might find we had to choose between loyalty to Christ and love for our family, but God never means us to act in a way that contradicts the principles laid down all through the Bible. We musn't take a single verse and quote it as a reason for neglecting our normal Christian duties.'

'Meaning?'

'Our duty to love our wives and train our children in the Christian faith. Bringing up your children in the right way is God's work, just as much as running a youth club.'

'It rather amuses me,' Eileen said, 'the way we Christians go on about the family, and how important family life is. We're very self-righteous about the terrible harm done to children if the mother is unmarried or divorced, and yet most of the young mums at our church get left to bring the kids up almost single-handed.'

'A slight exaggeration,' Dennis remarked, 'and anyway, I'm not sure that our two are old enough to need me yet. When they're in their teens it will be different.'

'At which point you'll kindly be around so that they can immediately pour out all their secret hopes and fears to you, I suppose,' Eileen said, sarcastically.

'What are you getting at?' Dennis asked, 'I certainly hope they will talk to me.'

'Eileen's quite right—that sort of relationship can't be built overnight,' Jack said. 'You can't decide to be a good father at a particular age and expect the children to respond. If you want to be close to them in their teens, you must get to know them now and spend some time with them—bath them, play with them and tuck them up in bed—pray with them occasionally too.'

'Yes,' Mrs. Peters agreed, 'I think children should find that Father comes, and not always Mother, when they wake up of an evening or a night. It's not good for the children or their mother if she can never be off duty.'

'Even when they're tiny, they need their father, I think,' Brenda said. 'I think a man gives them security and firmer discipline, as well as more fun and adventure in play.'

'I think they need both mother and father at every age,' Mrs. Peters said, 'but in different ways at different stages. You have to learn how to meet their needs in the right way, and that's not an easy job as they get older. They seem to grow up so quickly these days, but whatever they may pretend, they need you just as much in their teens as when they were tiny, and how close you've been in the early years has a lot to do with how much they take notice of you at the difficult stage.'

'I'm getting the impression now that you all think I should give up my Christian work and concentrate on being a good father,' Dennis commented.

'He's off again,' Eileen said, 'but now it's in the other direction. Isn't there such a thing as a middle course?'

'What—half the evenings out and the other half in?' Dennis suggested, with a laugh.

'Nothing as cut-and-dried as that,' Jack said, 'but a right balance between your Christian service in the church and in the home.'

'How can I find the right balance?'

I suppose it has to be worked out between you and

Sheila after real prayer and discussion. No one can criticize or advise other families—it's a personal decision.'

'But what factors should be considered?'

'If I could suggest something,' Mrs. Peters said, 'I would say it's worth putting by a certain time for the children each week—say, Saturday afternoon. After all, at this age they haven't any plans of their own, so they can fit in with the times you're free. Later on they'll have parties and football on Saturdays and they don't even thank you then for leaving an evening free to be with them. They just want you around in the background.'

'As far as evenings are concerned,' Brenda continued, 'we're lucky living here. Most fathers get home soon after five, so there is a chance to see the children then. When we lived near London and Jack had to travel miles each day, he hardly saw Rosemary at all, and he felt he had to do less at the church for a bit, so that he had some time to give her.'

'I don't go off in the evenings till it's their bedtime,' Dennis said, 'and I suppose if I left some of the older lads to open up at the club I could leave even later and I'd have time to help Sheila get them in.'

'Some of these older boys at church are quite responsible,' Brenda said, 'I believe they'd be only too willing to take on more responsibility if you gave them half a chance.'

'And trained them in the Carter Brown model methods,' Eileen added.

'I suppose I have tended to keep my own hand on the controls,' Dennis admitted. 'I honestly don't realize how these boys have grown up in the last couple of years.'

'I'm sure after a while they'd be able to take over in an emergency, such as last night,' Brenda agreed. 'Our Rosemary would willingly give a hand with the younger girls, if you asked her.'

'Thanks,' Dennis said; 'at this rate my own kids are going to have me around so much that they'll be sick of the sight of me.'

'They'll still see less of you than if you weren't a Christian,' Eileen insisted. 'No Sundays at the seaside or weekends in the caravan for them.'

'I don't know,' Brenda said, 'there are plenty of fathers I know who spend Sunday on the golf course.

'Or doing overtime to get extra pay,' Mrs. Peters added.

'Then you don't think there's much risk that children will grow up resenting their parents being busy with church work?' Eileen asked, 'or even turning against the Christian faith because of it?'

'Not if the balance is properly kept,' Jack said. 'I'm sure no child wants his parents revolving round him all the time. He wants some freedom to live his own life and should understand that his parents have work and interests outside the home, too. Anyway, it's right that he should see them putting their beliefs into action.'

'Mind you,' Brenda reminded him, 'there was a stage, when Rosemary was younger, when the amount of Christian work we had on made us so tired that we weren't putting our faith into action in the way we behaved at home or treated Rosemary. I was cross and impatient and you were . . . '

'Quite, I remember,' Jack agreed quickly, 'and I believe we cut down on activities at church so that we were able to cope physically. I might say it's a lot harder giving a job up than taking one on, but it sometimes needs to be done.'

'To get back to myself, if you don't mind,' Dennis said, 'I think I can see a few alterations I could make to my programme which should mean that I see a bit more of our two. I'll try to leave Saturdays clear and go out a bit later on club nights. I'll be able to see the kids into bed and then it won't matter if I get back later than usual.'

'Unless Sheila minds,' Eileen said. 'I suppose wives come in for a bit of consideration as well as children.'

Dennis looked surprised.

'We usually get a baby-sitter, and she comes here with me every other week, so she doesn't stay at home all the time.'

'Well, why couldn't you let her come tonight?' Eileen went on. 'I'm sure your mum would have liked a chat with you.'

'I honestly never thought of that,' Dennis said.

'I don't think men realize how you long to get away from the house and the children sometimes,' Brenda said, 'and Sheila is so gifted and loves to be sociable, too.'

'I was thinking about your Friday evening school lecture,' Jack said, 'couldn't Sheila do that for you? She's a chemist too, isn't she? Even if it isn't convenient for her to work in the day, she could do some teaching at night. It might give her an outlet during these years she's so tied to the sink.'

'I suppose I could look into the possibility,' Dennis agreed doubtfully.

'You know we've really arranged your lives very nicely for you,' Eileen said, 'I hope you're grateful.'

Dennis laughed, 'I expect I've asked for it.'

'But really we shouldn't,' Brenda said anxiously; 'there are too many people interfering and criticizing others. Everyone must work out his own responsibilities.'

She got up and began to fetch the coffee cups.

'Perhaps I ought not to stay,' Dennis suggested. 'I mean, I could get back and have a cup of tea with Mother and Sheila,' and he began to move towards the door.

'Better still, you could get it for them,' Eileen called after him.

'I don't think he heard,' Jack remarked as the front door closed, 'and a good job too. He's taken quite enough for one evening.'

SOME QUESTIONS TO THINK ABOUT

Are we, as husband and wife, in full agreement as to the time each gives to Christian work outside the home?

Do I give enough time to the care and training of the children God has given me?

Is the bringing up of the family a joint matter, shared by husband and wife?

Do I, as a husband, show thought and consideration for my wife during the years in which she is so much at home, looking after the children?

SOME VERSES TO HELP

'If anyone comes to Me without "hating" his father and mother and wife and children and brothers and sisters, and even his own life, he cannot be a disciple of Mine' (Luke 14. 26, Phillips).

'He who loves son or daughter more than Me is not

worthy of Me' (Matt. 10. 37, Phillips).

Fathers, don't over-correct your children or make it difficult for them to obey the commandment. Bring them up with Christian teaching in Christian discipline (Eph. 6. 4, Phillips).

Men ought to give their wives the love they naturally have for their own bodies. The love a man gives his wife is the extending of his love for himself to enfold her (Eph. 5. 28, Phillips).

You husbands should try to understand the wives you live with, honouring them as physically weaker yet equally heirs with you of the grace of life. If you don't do this, you will find it impossible to pray properly (1 Pet. 3. 7, Phillips).

Chapter 5

MY BOY WOULD NEVER DO THAT

'WHERE have Mr. and Mrs. Peters got to?' Sheila asked, as the rest of the group settled down in the Thomas' drawing-room.

'They're up to their eyes stocktaking or something,' Brenda said. 'I'm not very clear what that involves, except that they have to work on every evening at the moment. Mrs. Peters 'phoned to tell me about it and then, to my surprise, she rang again at tea-time and asked if she could come for half-an-hour after all, as there was something she wanted to talk about. She sounded terribly upset.'

At that moment the door bell rang and Mrs. Peters arrived. She was out of breath and looked flushed and red-eyed.

'I can't stay more than a few minutes,' she began, when Brenda had settled her in a comfortable armchair.

'You just tell us what's worrying you, if that will help at all.'

'Thank you, Mrs. Thomas, that would be a real relief. I hope I'm not wrong to tell you about our bit of trouble—Fred mightn't like it if he knew— but I know I can trust you all to keep a confidence and it will help me to talk about it. Fred's still very angry with our John and I feel so ashamed and concerned about him too, but I'd better tell you from the start. This afternoon Mr. Hutchinson—that's John's teacher—called in at the shop. He often does pop in for an *Echo* on his way home, so I wasn't bothered. There was no one else in the shop at the time, and he said to me,

' "I hope you didn't worry about John being late home yesterday, Mrs. Peters. Has he told you the reason yet?"

'I had to say I'd heard nothing from John, and just then Mr. Peters came back into the shop and heard what was going on.

' "Perhaps I'd better tell you about it," he said, "because your lad and young Jackson will end up in real trouble if they aren't careful. I've had my suspicions about what was going on for some time, but yesterday I caught four of them playing poker for money."

'What he said next I couldn't tell you. It was such a shock, what he'd told us, that I didn't take anything more in for a bit. I felt all at once so ashamed and disappointed and concerned for our John. Then Fred said,

' "Are you sure you're not making a mistake, Mr. Hutchinson? We won't have a pack of playing cards in our house, and I've taught my children never to touch them. As for gambling, I've taught them the evils of that from the cradle up."

'Then Mr. Hutchinson smiled—not meaning it unkindly, I'm sure—and said,

' "Well, someone's taught him a bit different, I'm afraid. There's no mistake, Mr. Peters, and from the money I made Hunt and Snell turn out of their pockets, I should say your boy and Reg Jackson had been losing badly. Well, gambling, as you would call it, is against school rules, so I had the four of them up to my room for a good dressing down. Can you tell me if John has been asking for extra money these last few weeks? I'm anxious to know how far this thing has gone."

'I couldn't seem to think properly then, but later, after he'd gone, I remembered saying to our John just last week that he always seems to be short of money. He's asked me for some so many times in the last month or two; he said it was for some school fund or trip. Then Fred told Mr. Hutchinson he'd give John a real good hiding when he came home, but he said John would get his punishment at school and that would be sufficient. He talked about his dad and me needing to show understanding, and it not being the lad's fault altogether, but Fred doesn't hold with these psychology ideas, as he calls them.

45

It just so happened that John had fixed to go over to Southborough straight after school, so we haven't seen him yet. What to do with him when we do, I just don't know. What can have made him behave like this?'

'It's pretty normal for boys of John's age to want to rebel against their parents' views,' Dennis suggested. 'He'd probably not be developing naturally if he went on toeing the line laid down at home. Young people have got to learn to be independent sooner or later, and in their efforts to be themselves, and not just an extension of their parents, they often go further than they need—go in for the very things their parents are dead against.'

'Oh, I know they get a bit headstrong in their teens,' Mrs. Peters agreed. 'John will often try cheeking me and he even likes to take the opposite view to what his dad thinks. But to do something wrong like gambling . . . '

'It may have been because all the other boys did it and he didn't like to feel different. He might be scared the others would call him a prig if he didn't join in,' Eileen suggested.

'Yes, I can well remember the agony of feeling I was different when I was a teenager,' Sheila agreed. 'I wasn't allowed to watch half the TV programmes the others did and was made to go to bed at what I thought was a ridiculously early hour. I used to invent all sorts of excuses rather than let on I was different or that my parents had odd ideas, as the others would think.'

'It's one thing for parents to have puritanical views, but it's quite another to enforce them on their children,' Dennis said. 'Why should children suffer

46

because of their parents' principles?'

'But the rules are for his good,' Mrs. Peters pleaded. 'There are some things his dad doesn't like, of course—like him getting these pop records or letting his hair grow long—but I sometimes turn a blind eye. As you say, I don't want him to feel out of it with the other lads. But gambling is different. It's wrong, and Fred has told him so many a time.'

'But has he explained why?' Dennis asked, a little impatiently. 'Does he realize in what way it's different from the other things Mr. Peters may say are wrong—like pop and having his hair long?'

'I agree,' went on Dennis, 'we must give reasons for our views of what's right or wrong, and not be too dictatorial when we lay down the law. I know it's because we're so afraid that our children will run into trouble that we give it to them hot and strong, but human nature is a funny thing. If we're told loud enough and often enough *not* to do a thing, it only makes us want to do it all the more. We stand a better chance of having our advice followed if we offer it calmly and quietly, without emotion, giving the reasons why we think the way we do. Perhaps John has grown up with a kind of superstitious belief that a pack of playing cards was a forbidden evil, and yet had no idea of the kind of trouble he could get into if he started playing for money. At least he's learned now—even though it's the hard way. He's a sensible lad, and he'll see for himself that it's a mug's game—more losing than winning. He'll realize the kind of trouble it can land him in, too, deceiving you and having to be dishonest.'

'That's what I can't understand,' Mrs. Peters said, 'why he didn't come straight and tell us once he was in trouble over losing money. If only he'd come and owned up, we'd have understood and helped him.'

'Was he to know that?' Dennis asked. 'I mean, he knows your husband's views on the subject. He was probably scared to let on.'

'But he's not afraid of *me*,' Mrs. Peters pleaded.

'He might be afraid of upsetting you,' Brenda suggested, 'and being a disappointment to you or even losing your love. I know that's not really possible, but it might seem so to him, you know.'

'You have to teach them that you feel strongly about right and wrong, yet at the same time let them be absolutely sure that nothing they do will ever stop you loving them and standing by them,' Jack said, 'but I'm sure that's what you've done with John.'

'I've tried to, and yet somehow I feel I've been lacking,' Mrs. Peters said, 'and it may be through some fault of mine that he's gone wrong.'

'Parents are always made to feel guilty nowadays,' Brenda said; 'whatever we do is wrong, according to the experts. We've either been too strict or too lenient, fussed over them or neglected them. We just can't win. I think that's only a half-truth and that young people are responsible for their own actions.'

'But there's one thing on my mind,' Mrs. Peters persisted, 'the fact that I've not given the time to John that I gave to our other four. Do you know, when Mr. Hutchinson asked if I'd worried over John being late home from school, I realized I'd never even noticed him being late, with the shop being so busy. I haven't the time to take an interest in his hobbies and that.'

'It's funny how much they still need you in their

48

teens,' Brenda said. 'I've found that with Rosemary. In a way they make more demands on you than when they were tiny, because now they want all your attention, not just someone to bandage up a sore knee or wash their clothes for them. They want to talk, to share life with you as a friend and not just a parent. It makes you think all over again about some of the problems you've shelved since your own youth.'

'Of course, some parents never do establish this kind of relationship with the children,' Dennis said. 'Development has been arrested at the washing clothes and dishing out pocket-money stage.'

'It takes time and trouble getting to know your teenagers as people in their own right,' Jack said.

'Yes, Mr. Thomas, and that's where I'm afraid I've failed. It was different with our other four. They were all close in age and I was always at home ready to listen to all their little problems or successes. They brought home friends who fitted in with the things we did. I suppose I'm not as young now as I was then. I remember, when I knew our John was on the way, I felt tired at the thought of going through all those stages again. You see, by the time he was at school the eldest two were married and the other two left home before he was much older. It's been lonely for him and he's always been a quiet lad and kept himself to himself.'

'There must be problems for a child who is a late arrival,' Brenda agreed.

'But there are problems for every child, according to his place in the family,' Dennis reasoned. 'It's tough on an eldest, because his parents have to experiment with him a bit and he's always the first to face the different milestones in life. The youngest has to watch everyone else having privileges and new experiences before he does.'

'And middle ones have it worst of all, I think,' Brenda added; 'they get none of the attention of an eldest or the petting a youngest gets.'

'I'm an only one,' Dennis went on, 'and that has its disadvantages too. It's not that you're necessarily spoiled, but you get too many grown-ups concentrating on you and too much adult talk and goings-on around you, too.

'In other words, every child has some problem to cope with whether he's first, last or only one. We parents ought to realize this and be on the look-out for anything we can do to help the child get over the particular disadvantages of his position in the family. It's no good treating them as if they all start life on the same footing.'

'Of course, in a way, it's been easier for John,' Mrs. Peters went on. 'We've not been badly off like we were when the others were young. I've been pleased I could give him the things he was wanting, when it had all been scrimp and pinch with the other four. Perhaps I've thought the extra money made up for the time and interest he really needed. Too much money come by too easily may be a bad thing. It may have helped to lead him into this trouble. I've made up my mind I'm going to give our John a bit more home life. It's like we were saying the other week about working wives. It can be the children who suffer—and not just the toddlers and babies, but the older ones too. You can be so busy with your job that the home hardly looks lived in. The lad often eats his tea by himself, then goes on out while I'm busy in the shop. It all started when we opened the business—we had to keep open all hours to oblige and couldn't afford extra help. It's different now, and I must tell Fred so. If I can be around and the place warm and cheerful, John might do like our others did, and bring his mates back to our place, instead of always being out. He'll feel we really love him and want him then.

'I'd better be getting along now—I want a talk with Fred before the lad gets home. We've got to stand together in this and how we talk to him now is going to count. I know what he really needs—to trust in Christ for himself—that's what me and Fred have always prayed for, and it's the only way for him to want to go straight and to have the strength to. Thank you for listening to my troubles and for the things you've said to help as well.'

* * * * * *

'Well, old Peters has asked for this lot,' Dennis announced, when Mrs. Peters had left.

'Thank goodness you didn't actually say so in front of poor Mrs. Peters. She's taking the whole thing so much to heart.'

'He's enough to make any self-respecting teenager go clean off the lines,' Dennis grumbled on.

'Because he's so strict?' Brenda asked.

'Yes—this "thou-shalt-not-because-I-say-so" stuff won't wash these days.'

'Still, parents need to be firm sometimes,' Brenda said, 'I mean, there must be just as many children from Christian homes who've gone wrong through too little discipline as through too much.'

'Of course firmness and discipline are necessary,'

51

Jack agreed, 'and far too many parents are too lazy or weak to put their foot down where they should.'

'But it's no good having too many rules,' Sheila said; 'surely they should be kept to the minimum and a parent's prejudices on topics like clothes, music and so on shouldn't be confused with basic rules of right and wrong?'

'I believe the most important thing any parents can do is to teach their children to think for themselves,' Dennis said. 'Give them reasons for your views and way of life from the very start, and teach them to think out their views from scratch. If you don't do that, you'll either produce polly parrots, or rebels.'

'I say, I feel I ought to clap or cheer or something,' Eileen said. 'Anyway, I think you're right; I'd vote for you anyway, speech or no speech.'

Dennis laughed.

You know, you should get young John to your Youth Club,' Jack suggested; 'start him thinking for himself there.'

'Not a bad idea,' Dennis agreed; 'I may try and do just that.'

SOME QUESTIONS TO THINK ABOUT

Am I too busy to keep in touch with my teenagers?
Do I try to make up to them with money and gifts for the time I'm not willing to spare them?
Can they treat me as a friend as well as a parent?
Do I handle them with a right amount of firmness, or give in for the sake of a bit of peace?
Do I allow for the individual difficulties my children face because of their particular position in the family pattern?

Am I ready to face up to my shortcomings as a parent as well as to theirs as teenagers?

Do I help my children to understand the underlying value of moral codes, or lay down hard-and-fast rules to be obeyed?

Do I make an effort to understand the problems and temptations of a generation different from my own?

Do we, as husband and wife, pray and act together for our children?

SOME VERSES TO HELP

Train up a child in the way he should go: and when he is old, he will not depart from it (Prov. 22. 6, AV).

Fathers, don't over-correct your children or make it difficult for them to obey the commandment. Bring them up with Christian teaching in Christian discipline (Eph. 6. 4, Phillips).

Fathers, don't over-correct your children, or they will grow up feeling inferior and frustrated (Col. 3. 21, Phillips).

Don't worry over anything whatever: tell God every detail of your needs in earnest and thankful prayer, and the peace of God, which transcends human understanding, will keep constant guard over your hearts and minds as they rest in Christ Jesus (Phil. 4. 6, 7, Phillips).

Tremendous power is made available through a good man's earnest prayer (James 5. 16b, Phillips).

Chapter 6

MIDDLE-AGE WITHOUT
TEARS

'BRENDA says it's her turn to start the ball rolling tonight,' Jack Thomas began, when the group had all arrived. 'Mind you, I think it's only because there's something she's bursting to say. How about a subject from you next time, Eileen? That will be after the Spring holiday.'

'Unless an urgent problem crops up for anyone else,' Sheila said.

'No one's going to stop me having my go,' Eileen insisted. 'I'm going away for the week on holiday, so I'll have time to decide which of my many problems to worry you with. Come on, though, Mrs. Thomas, let's be hearing from you.'

'I was in the butcher's last Thursday,' Brenda began, 'and that young Mrs. Taylor from the other side of the Green was in the shop. The doctor's told her she's having twins and she's got two small children already, so she was having a light-hearted grumble—she's a happy-go-lucky, cheerful sort. Then, to my amazement, she said, "Of course, you'll have forgotten what it's like having them tiny, now you're middle-aged." I remembered the sort of woman I'd considered middle-aged when Rosemary was young, and couldn't believe I looked like that to her. When I got home I came straight upstairs and had a good look in the mirror. I tried to be honest about what I saw and pretend it was someone I didn't know, and I had to admit that she was right. I saw a typical middle-aged woman, hair going grey, furrowed brow, lines round the mouth, drawn and worried-looking.'

'I say, I must lend you this week's *Home & Beauty*, Mrs. Thomas. It's got a step-by-step aid to youthful glamour,' Eileen said.

'But we wouldn't want you all youth and glamour, Brenda,' Dennis protested.

'What a back-hander!' Sheila said, 'I do apologize for my husband.'

'A Christian woman should grow old gracefully,' Mr. Peters said seriously; 'dyed hair and painted face are not for her. She should look as God meant her to be.'

Brenda giggled weakly. 'You're all making me feel in the last stages of decay,' she complained, 'but this whole question of beauty aids is one I wanted to talk about. I suppose I have neglected my looks lately, and my weight, too, and I thought I ought to do something about it.'

'Of course you should,' Eileen agreed. 'I've read all about it. You need a good nourishing skin food and something to condition your hair. And cooking for a family means you've probably been eating too much of the wrong kind of food for ages—so you need a special diet. You probably need too to change completely the type of make-up you use.'

'Oh, for goodness' sake!' Sheila broke in. 'We know that's what the women's magazines all say, but no one is going to be taken in by the results and think you're half the age you really are. I feel strongly on this subject. I think it's a wicked waste of money and time, trying to regain a lost youth.'

'You mean, Christians shouldn't bother so much about their looks?' Eileen asked. 'I think it's important to look as smart and attractive as you can, whatever age you are, and that's bound to cost a bit, in time and money.'

'Oh, yes, within limits,' Sheila agreed, 'but when you think of the millions in the world who are starving or diseased, and then of the money middle-aged women squander on their faces and figures . . . '

'I would have thought it was all a matter of moderation,' Jack said mildly. 'There is a happy medium. I don't want a wife who's dowdy or down-at-heel, but I'm not keen on blue rinses and that sort of thing, either. Not that I know much about it.'

'No, you don't, Jack,' Sheila said decidedly. 'You think of the whole thing as trivial and even vaguely amusing from your masculine heights. But there's an important principle involved. These women who spend so much time on their appearance are trying to be young all over again, and it just isn't on.'

'I know what you mean, dear,' Mrs. Peters agreed. 'They don't like facing up to being middle-aged. They've forgotten all the miserable times in youth when you're shy or don't know the right things to say or do. They just want to go back to the nice bits of being young. That seems to me a bit like refusing what God wants to give us—the next stage of the journey, so to speak. There are lots of joys in middle-age—though maybe they're different from those of youth—and there are responsibilities to face up to as well. I often think middle-age is the busiest time in life, with teenagers to look after and the old ones needing us often too. We ought not to run away from all that by trying to be young over again.'

'Yet, at the same time, you should stay young in the sense of welcoming new ideas and being adaptable,' Dennis insisted.

'Yes,' Eileen agreed, 'so often being middle-aged is the same thing as turning into a fossil. You know what some of them are like at church. They won't hear of the slightest change being made in the routine and think everything should go on in the way it did thirty years ago. They have a fit if someone sits in the pew they've occupied for the last I don't know how many years.'

'It's the same over what they hear from the pulpit,' Dennis went on; 'anything different from what they're used to just isn't allowed to penetrate. They've made up their minds on all subjects and they're not prepared to have a fresh think about anything. I can't see people like that being any use in a work for God. A Christian church is something alive—it's always growing and changing, and the members of it must grow and change too, if they're not to be a hindrance.'

'I don't think that's happened to me yet,' Brenda said, 'I don't feel exactly fossilized, but I do feel somehow empty of ideas or inspiration. Life seems a bit of a desert—no future in anything. I find I keep looking back on the old days, when Rosemary was tiny. I know there were plenty of problems; money was short and I was always terribly busy, but the days were full and there was so much to look forward to. Now . . . '

'You must need a tonic, darling,' Jack said.

'I suppose it does sound morbid, and not very Christian either,' Brenda agreed. 'It's probably to do with Rosemary leaving home. London seems so far away, and although I know she's happy enough, everything here seems so flat.'

'I know I've felt upset every time one of mine has left home,' Mrs. Peters agreed, 'and it must be that much worse with your only child.'

'I think that a woman ought to find some new interest or outlet for her energies before her children leave,' Sheila said.

'No doubt you'll return to your teaching career,' Brenda replied, then added quickly, 'I'm afraid that sounded catty, but those of us who aren't career women do feel a bit useless once our children don't need us. We've made home-making our whole life, not just one string to our bow.'

Sheila said nothing but looked round appreciatively at the room, at the unscratched paintwork, the beautiful flower arrangements and the many signs that the home was cared for and loved. At present she had the excuse of young children, but she knew in her heart that her own home would never look that way. Brenda's house must always have been artistic and harmonious even when Rosemary was little and times less easy. But she realized, too, that, unlike Brenda, she would never find life dull or uneventful or be at a loss for work, not because of her career, as Brenda called it, but because of her temperament. No doubt middle-age brought different problems to different people.

'What do you think I ought to do with my life now, Mrs. Peters?' Brenda asked.

'It seems to me that during all those busy years when you were young—though you still seem young to me, dear—you were gathering experience— experience of life and experience of the way God leads us and cares for us. Now you can use that experience to help others. You have so much to give and there are so many people in need. You haven't come to the end, you're just beginning a new chapter in life.'

'I suppose it ought to be exciting and challenging,' Brenda said doubtfully, 'if I only knew what the next chapter ought to have in it.'

'I think maybe you need a little holiday first,' Mrs. Peters suggested. 'At your age you often get a bit run-down and depressed and a change might do you a world of good. After that you can think about how to use your time and gifts.'

'I think Christians should give more time to voluntary work,' Sheila said. 'There's marriage guidance work, the Samaritan service, as well as hospital work—taking round books, making tea in out-patients' departments, or visiting psychiatric patients.'

'Aren't they needing another leader for the Young Wives' Group at church?' Eileen asked.

'Perhaps I *shall* need a holiday,' Brenda said, 'but at least I've a few ideas to think about and I'll pray about them too. Maybe I've been a bit too cosy in my nice little nest these last few years.'

'It's easy to be too taken up with bodily comforts as you get older,' Mr. Peters warned.

'I think you're right,' Jack agreed. 'I suppose we feel we've earned the right to relax and be comfortable after all the struggles of the past years. It's nice to enjoy things and be able to afford a bit more.'

'Your tastes certainly do get more expensive as you get older,' Dennis said. 'I'm discovering that already. It's easy just to put your standards higher as your salary goes up, instead of thinking out how much it's right to spend on luxuries and things for yourself.'

'I'd have thought you were entitled to a bit of luxury by the time you're middle-aged,' Eileen observed.

'We don't need any encouraging,' Jack said, 'we need to be reminded to get on with the job of Christian living. It would do us good to be shaken up a bit and thrown into action. I've known people who've gone overseas to do missionary work after they've retired, or chucked up safe jobs with pensions to have a go in some new Christian venture. I know we can't all do anything so dramatic, but at least we can wake up our ideas a bit and be ready to tackle something new.'

'Yes, and like I said, there's usually a lot to do

ready to hand,' Mrs. Peters said, 'if you haven't elderly parents to care for, or a string of teenagers of your own to keep an eye on; these's usually young and old all around needing help. It's nice to be needed, and it's my experience that middle-aged folk usually are. I think the Lord has special work for us to do at this time in our life.'

'Perhaps so,' said Brenda. 'I know I've got to come to terms with these feelings and have the courage to get going again. Even God has seemed a bit unreal to me lately. I want to find Him in a new way. I can't exist on the past—the experiences I had as a young Christian. I want God to mean something in this new bit of my life, not just be a kind of extra that I take for granted. I feel as if I need a new vision of what God can mean to me and of what I can do with my life to be useful and satisfied again. It's a coming to terms with myself and with God's purpose in my life, I suppose. I think it's the most important thing I've got to do.'

SOME QUESTIONS TO THINK ABOUT

How far am I right to spend time and money 'staying young'?

Do I close my mind to new ideas or changes in the life of my church?

Have I become so wrapped up in my family that I have no other interests or outlet for my service?

Am I spending more on myself and material things, or giving more to God?'

Is God real to me? Has my experience of Him developed and matured as I have grown older?

Am I willing at any time to change the settled pattern of my life, if God should call me to do so?

61

Am I willing to step down from some forms of service, in order to give responsibility to younger people? Or am I clinging to a job because I'm afraid that, if I give it up, I shall feel unwanted?

SOME VERSES TO HELP

Your beauty should not be dependent on an elaborate coiffure, or on the wearing of jewellery or fine clothes, but on the inner personality—the unfading loveliness of a calm and gentle spirit, a thing very precious in the eyes of God (1 Pet. 3. 3, 4, Phillips).

Men who set their hearts on being wealthy expose themselves to temptation . . . For loving money leads to all kinds of evil, and some men in the struggle to be rich have lost their faith and caused themselves untold agonies of mind. But you, the man of God, keep clear of such things. Set your heart not on riches, but on goodness, Christ-likeness, faith, love, patience and humility. Fight the worthwhile battle of the faith (1 Tim. 6. 9-12, Phillips).

Never give your hearts to this world or to any of the things in it (1 John 2. 15, Phillips).

Bear one another's burdens, and so fulfil the law of Christ (Gal. 6. 2, RSV).

Let us strip off everything that hinders us, as well as the sin which dogs our feet, and let us run the race that we have to run with patience, our eyes fixed on Jesus the source and the goal of our faith (Heb. 12. 1, 2, Phillips).

They who wait for the Lord shall renew their strength, they shall mount up with wings like eagles, they shall run and not be weary, they shall walk and not faint (Isa. 40. 31, RSV).

Chapter 7

WHEN DOES THE HONEYMOON STOP?

'Enjoyed your holiday, Eileen?' Sheila asked, when the group met again after the holiday break.

'Yes, I suppose so, though I felt worried about George and Doreen—they're the friends I stayed with. In fact I'm going to leave all my own little problems, and ask you all what you think about the Christian views on marriage.'

'I say, what's this?' Jack asked, as he came in and closed the door.

'Don't get excited, Mr. Thomas; I haven't started courting. Not that I've given up hope yet. But it's someone else's problem I want to talk about—it's got me worried.'

They all settled down to listen, and Eileen began her story.

'I don't think any of you really knew George and Doreen. I got to know them when we were all helpers at the Grangeburn Youth Camps. Then George got moved to the Midlands with his job. I remember how I used to tease them the first time I stayed with them after they were married. They were all "lovey-dovey", sitting together on the settee holding hands, you know. In a way it made me feel an odd one out, though I'm sure they didn't realize it then. But the next time I went they seemed to think about me more. They were just as keen about each other, but they seemed to want to spread their happiness and love to include me, if you can understand. I haven't seen them for a couple of years since that visit, so I was really looking forward to last week. Then, when I got there, everything seemed different. Doreen met me on her own—said George was busy gardening. He stayed out working till it was dark, then he wanted a programme on the telly that Doreen wasn't interested in, so we drank tea in the kitchen while he watched it. It was like that all the week-end, although of course we went to church and so on together. It doesn't sound much now I've put it in words, but everything seemed different, as I said before. In the old days we always made a joke of the way they shared the jobs and stayed together. They'd been so wrapped up in each other, and now they seemed two quite separate people who happened to be living under the same roof. Well, you know me, I can't keep my big mouth shut. By Monday I felt I had to get it off my chest to Doreen—which I did.'

'Fools rush in!' Dennis muttered.

'Well, I tried to be tactful,' Eileen said, 'but I suppose she did choke me off a bit. She said they weren't honeymooners any longer. She didn't seem to want to hear what I remembered of my last stay, and how they'd got over the sloppy stage but still loved each other a lot. She said of course they still loved each other, but that you couldn't live in each other's pockets the whole time and that she had her own life and her own interests to think of as well as George's. She said at least they weren't always having rows like Brian and Shirley. They're another couple who live down the road and go to the same church. They behaved in a childish way, she thought, either all over each other or in the middle of a bust-up. She seemed to prefer to talk about them than about herself and George. She ended up by saying that if I ever got married (a nasty crack) I might understand better. After that I couldn't very well say any more. It's shaken me up, though. Doreen and George aren't exactly on the rocks with their marriage, and yet they don't seem to me to be what a Christian couple should be.'

'You're a disillusioned woman?' Dennis asked.

'It's all very well to tease, but I'm serious. I know that lots of people who aren't Christians have unhappy marriages—I've seen some. But I always imagined that a Christian marriage would be ideal, like George and Doreen's seemed at first, and I can't understand it.'

'It's not all that surprising if as Christians we sometimes fail in our marriages, as in everything else in life, just because we are human. Both partners can be selfish or have annoying faults that spoil things,' Jack explained.

'But I thought love was supposed to be the answer,' Eileen argued.

'It is, of course,' Jack went on, 'but I'm afraid self-love is often stronger than love for the other person.'

'Yet you do hear of couples saying they've never had a cross word,' Brenda suggested doubtfully.

'I'm naturally suspicious of them,' Sheila said. 'They've probably forgotten a few incidents in the long-lost past.'

'Or one of them regularly gives in to the other, which isn't a good thing,' Dennis added.

'Aren't you all cynics!' Eileen complained.

'Not really,' Jack assured her, 'but we are trying to be realists. Pretending that it's easy to achieve the very best and highest in Christian marriage is no way to bring it about. It's far better to face up to the possible difficulties beforehand.'

'I agree,' Sheila said, 'and I believe that a lot of the big problems that crop up and can spoil a marriage are matters that should have been thrashed out long before the wedding.'

'For example?' Eileen asked.

'When to have a family, or whether the wife goes on working indefinitely. Family planning methods, too.'

'And which church they join,' Dennis suggested.

'And how they'll budget their income and share their money,' Brenda added.

'Quite a few points of difference do crop up after marriage, even so,' Dennis said, 'you don't always allow for the fact that different upbringing and temperament are going to give you very different outlooks on things like spending money, educating the children and so on.'

'It's children that keep a marriage together,' Mr. Peters insisted. 'Your friends, Eileen, need a little family.'

Sheila and Dennis exchanged glances and laughed.

'We've often said just the opposite,' Sheila explained. 'We've come nearer to blows on the subject of our kids than anything else.'

'But they stop you getting too selfish or set in your ways,' Brenda said.

'I agree really, but half the trouble is that you get so tired when the children are tiny. You lose so much sleep when they're ill or teething, and they're a strain in the daytime too, I find. Then you have church activities and your husband's business worries to cope with on top of that, and the result is that you get cross and irritable with each other.'

'There are certainly some stages in your married life when you need to take special care and to readjust to each other where necessary,' Jack observed.

'Yes,' Mrs. Peters agreed, 'when the first baby comes along it's easy for Mother to get taken up with him, and then poor Father feels left out. When the children grow up, too, a marriage seems to change. You have time to be together more again and you have to find a new way of life together.'

'Not every couple makes these adjustments very easily or smoothly,' Jack said. 'Some never seem to make them at all, and that's where trouble comes. Often there are periods of weeks or months, or even longer, when the relationship is not at its best.'

'Yet I've never heard Christians admit in so many words that their marriage isn't perfect,' Eileen complained. 'That seems dishonest to me.'

'I suppose we take a firm line against divorce and

67

adultery or anything that threatens marriage, and so it almost goes against our vested interests to admit there are faults and failures in our own marriage,' Sheila suggested.

'I think it's more that we feel we're letting the Christian side down by admitting that our marriage is anything less than perfect. We've been brought up to believe that Christian marriage should work, so we think we ought to prove that it does.'

'People do try to be loyal to their husbands or wives,' Brenda said. 'That's another thing that stops them talking to other people about their failures.'

'But a husband and wife ought to be absolutely honest with each other,' Sheila said decidedly. 'It's fatal to kid yourself that things are all right because you won't face up to the fact that you've failed, and need to put things right.'

'Supposing,' Eileen said slowly, 'you discovered that you'd made a mistake—married someone you didn't love or couldn't get on with, I don't think it's like that with George and Doreen, mind you, but it could happen, couldn't it?'

'If you both love the Lord,' Mr. Peters began . . .

'That doesn't necessarily mean you're suited to spend your life together,' Sheila said.

'No,' Jack agreed, 'it *is* possible for one or both partners of a Christian marriage to find they've made a mistake. I'm sure God guides us in choosing who we marry, so if we've made a mistake like that, it will be our own fault, because we haven't brought God into it from the very start in some way or another.'

'But God is bigger than our mistakes,' Brenda said, 'and I think this is true over lots of decisions we make in life. If we admit we've gone wrong and ask His help, He can make something good even out of the mess we've landed ourselves in. It would be a pretty awful thing to have to go through though. But George and Doreen haven't that sort of heart-break—they sound as though they're well suited, Eileen. Perhaps they're just in need of a helping hand.'

'Not from me—they made that clear,' Eileen said.

'Well, people ought to get professional advice about marriage problems when they need to,' Sheila said.

'But you couldn't go to people who wouldn't understand the Christian attitude,' Brenda protested.

'Then there should be more help from Christian advisers—in books and articles, or at week-end conferences and that kind of thing,' Sheila said.

'It's wonderful how prayer can solve problems,' Mrs. Peters said. 'Praying for each other and praying together seem to make such a difference, we've found, even to the biggest problem. We have outside help that the unbeliever knows nothing of.'

'So if there's a difference of opinion over any matter, you believe that a Christian couple should pray for the right answer, do you?' Eileen asked.

Before Mrs. Peters could reply, her husband said, 'Yes, provided the wife remembers her duty to obey her husband. It's for her to submit.'

'He's a sort of senior partner, yes, I agree,' Sheila said, 'but I don't believe God meant husbands to use their authority to override their wives in every choice that comes along.'

'In other words,' Jack said, 'we come back to the good old phrase "give and take". If a marriage is going to succeed, both sides have to give way at times. The New Testament tells husbands to love their wives and to understand them, and wives to adapt themselves to their husbands. I wonder if your two friends haven't quite learned that lesson yet, Eileen.'

'I'm quite sure they haven't. But I'd still like to know if Doreen was right in saying that when you really can't agree it's better to go your separate ways than to quarrel. What do you think?'

'I think a good row clears the air,' Sheila said, 'and it's so nice afterwards. You end up feeling extra close and quite ready to admit that the other one is right and that you've been a beast.'

'I think rows can do terrible damage,' Brenda said, 'you say such dreadful things and because you know each other so completely you can hurt in the most sensitive spots. You can't forget some of the things that are said and you'd give anything to unsay your own words. A bad row seems to destroy in a minute something between you that you've been carefully building for years.'

'Isn't there a difference between rows that clear the air, like a thunder-storm, leaving everything fresh and ready for a new start, with no hard feelings on either side, and those that result from a deep-down disturbance in the marriage?' Dennis suggested. 'Most couples would recognize the difference. Where there are really bitter rows pretty frequently, there's probably an underlying grievance that ought to be dealt with. The rows are symptoms of something more serious that needs putting right.'

'I must say that in a way I think drifting apart *is* more serious than the occasional row,' Jack said.

'Our Lord taught that in marriage two people become one, at every level of their being. This is a difficult ideal to achieve, but to take the line of going separate ways instead is to admit complete failure. A couple who does that is missing all that God meant marriage to be.'

'I suppose you have to be on the look-out and stop the drift in the early stages,' Eileen suggested.

'A good marriage doesn't just happen,' Mrs. Peters agreed; 'like everything worthwhile it takes time and care and love if it's to flourish.'

'I often think that a marriage needs a bit of general maintenance if it's to be kept in running order,' Jack said. 'Husband and wife need to check every part of their relationship—physical, mental and spiritual—and make sure that there is real harmony on every level.'

'I'm sure a lot of Christians feel you should play down the physical side of the relationship, 'Sheila said, 'yet it's important that both husband and wife find satisfaction on that level. Maybe there is too much emphasis on sex today, but some Christians have tended to keep silent about the importance of sex to a happy marriage. It's better to get medical advice if either one is frustrated or disappointed because of an unsatisfactory physical relationship. With a bit of help things can often be put right easily.'

'I think it's important to share your thoughts and ideas too,' Dennis said. 'Sheila and I always tell each other every detail of the day's happenings—it helps us to keep close. Some couples seem completely out of touch with each other.'

'I think you should take a real interest in each

other's affairs,' Brenda said. 'Mine probably seem trivial to Jack, and his are a bit above my head, but we're both interested because it concerns each other.'

'For a Christian couple, it's the spiritual realm that matters most,' Mr. Peters said. 'It's wonderful to begin and end each day together in prayer and to study God's Word together too.'

'It's amazing how much we can help each other spiritually,' Sheila agreed.

'So don't feel too disillusioned, Eileen,' Jack said, 'and don't give up hope for George and Doreen either. Perhaps Christian marriages don't always achieve the best, but there's the means to do so within our grasp. We have a whole extra dimension—the power and presence of God—to make our marriage grow deeper and more satisfying and more useful to God as time goes by.'

QUESTIONS TO THINK ABOUT

Are there any unresolved problems in our marriage that need dealing with?

Are we making do with a second-best relationship, or aiming at the highest, intended by God?

Do I, as a husband, show love and understanding to my wife?

Do, I, as a wife, feel respect for my husband and adapt my way of life to his?

Are we both willing to give way to each other in love?

Do we, together, bring our problems to God in prayer?

Are we truly at every level of our life together?

Are we helping each other towards Christian maturity?

VERSES TO HELP

Jesus said . . . from the beginning of creation, God made them male and female. For this reason a man shall leave his father and mother and be joined to his wife, and the two shall become one. So they are no longer two but one. What therefore God has joined together, let not man put asunder (Mark 10. 6–9, RSV).

You wives must learn to adapt yourselves to your husbands, as you submit yourselves to the Lord, for the husband is the 'head' of the wife in the same way that Christ is Head of the Church and Saviour of His body. The willing subjection of the Church to Christ should be reproduced in the submission of wives to their husbands. But, remember, this means that the husband must give his wife the same sort of love that Christ gave to the Church, when He sacrificed Himself for her (Eph. 5. 22–25, Phillips).

Wives, adapt yourselves to your husbands, that your marriage may be a Christian unity. Husbands, be sure you give your wives much love and sympathy; don't let bitterness or resentment spoil your marriage (Col. 3. 18–19, Phillips).

Love knows no limit to its endurance, no end to its trust, no fading of its hope; it can outlast anything. It is, in fact, the one thing that still stands when all else has fallen (1 Cor. 13. 7–8a, Phillips).

Heirs together of the grace of life (1 Pet. 3. 7, AV).

Chapter 8

'BUT I ONLY TOLD SO-AND-SO (SO THAT SHE COULD PRAY INTELLIGENTLY)'

'COME on, Mr. Peters, it's your turn to start our discussion going this evening,' Brenda said, with an effort to be cheerful. Looking at Mr. Peters' stern countenance, she had a presentiment that all was not well. A quick glance at Mrs. Peters confirmed her fears.

'I'm sorry to have to raise a very unpleasant matter,' Mr. Peters began slowly. 'It's not for me to accuse anyone present here, but I can't help but feel that someone has been disloyal and betrayed a confidence—I speak for the wife and myself. She tells me now that when our boy, John, got himself in the wrong at his school, she came to you Christian friends and asked for your prayers. This was unknown to me. You will understand, I feel sure, that we want no kind of talk about our boy, however much we believe he did wrong. The next thing I know, Mr. Atkins, who lives up Rowan Drive, came into the shop and said he'd heard young John was going to be expelled for gambling. He'd heard, too, that there had been something suspicious about the way he'd got hold of the money to pay his debts. Mind, I'd rather he came and told me than passed the story on, though for all we know the tale has gone all round the roads here already. We feel it for the lad's sake, as his parents, but more so because of the harm done to the Christian witness in the village. Because we keep the shop we're well known all about, and most people know well enough the truths we stand for. Mother and I are always ready to say a word in season whenever we can. Now they can point the finger of scorn and unbelief.'

'What makes you think one of us is responsible for spreading the story?' Jack asked.

'You know we wouldn't let you down,' Brenda added; 'all we wanted to do was to be of help, and Mrs. Peters made it quite clear that what she told us was not to go beyond our little group.'

'We've told no one else,' Mr. Peters said, 'the schoolmaster wouldn't have done either.'

'And it can't be Mrs. Jackson—Reg's mother—because John says Reg hasn't told her anything about it,' Mrs. Peters added.

'Another thing is that I asked Jim Atkins where he heard the tale. He said his wife got it from Mrs. Robinson, and knowing she goes to church from time to time, that seemed the answer.'

'Well, when Mrs. Peters told us that night, I looked on it as I would a family matter—something where loyalty to each other as Christians was involved.'

'I agree with that,' Eileen said, 'though I'll admit that I did mention it, just to one other Christian friend. I wanted her to pray about it too. There was no harm in that, was there?'

'But Mrs. Peters specially asked us not to say anything about it to anyone else,' Brenda said.

'Well, it was Christine I told,' Eileen continued, 'Christine Dobson, you know. We go round together quite a bit because she's in the typing pool at work. Seeing she's a Christian I thought she'd be able to pray about it like we were. Of course I told her not to let it go any further, and I'm sure I can trust her.'

'Like Mrs. Peters trusted you?' Dennis asked. Eileen flushed angrily and turned to Brenda.

'Mrs. Thomas, do you think I could use your 'phone? I'd like to speak to Christine and settle this matter straightaway.'

She went out into the hall, and to the others waiting rather silently, it seemed a long while before she returned, closed the door and sat quietly down again.

'I asked Christine point-blank if she'd passed on what I said to anyone, and she was quite indignant—said of course she hadn't. Then she added that she'd told her mother, of course, but she didn't count that

76

really. I soon told her I did count that and asked her to find out if her mother had told anyone else. She came back and said her mother only mentioned it to Mrs. Robinson, because she remembered she went to the same church as the Peters and thought she'd probably know about it anyway.'

'Mrs. Robinson and Mrs. Atkins both help with school meals, so that's where they had their little chat,' Mr. Peters said.

'Mrs. Robinson has no right to gossip like that about members of the church,' Eileen protested; 'she should have kept her mouth shut. I've heard of other trouble she's caused at church with her tittle-tattling.'

'Come off it, Eileen,' Dennis said, 'it's no good being full of righteous indignation against Mrs. Robinson, when you know perfectly well that you were responsible in the first place.'

'And the more the story is repeated, the more it's exaggerated,' Sheila said, 'so that it's not even the truth that's being gossiped round now.'

'Well, I had no thought of gossiping,' Eileen maintained, 'I really only meant Christine to pray.'

At that moment she caught sight of Mrs. Peters' face. It showed none of the anger of her husband, nor the intolerance of Dennis Carter Brown. Instead she returned Eileen's look with one of gentleness and affection, almost of pity. Eileen burst suddenly into tears. In a moment Mrs. Peters was beside her.

'My dear, we've been hard on you. We know you meant no harm to us.'

'I was stupid and thoughtless and I broke our promise,' Eileen wailed. 'I've let you down and it's all my fault.'

The rest of the group fidgeted uncomfortably. Then, as suddenly as she had begun, Eileen stopped crying. She got out a handkerchief, blew her nose and sat up straight.

'I'm sorry to make a scene,' she said, 'and I suppose you all feel awkward now. I didn't mean to, but it was seeing Mrs. Peters so kind and forgiving. While you were blaming me, the rest of you, I didn't feel like admitting I was wrong, but deep down I knew I was. First of all, I want to tell you how truly sorry I am, Mr. and Mrs. Peters. I really mean it— I wouldn't have willingly hurt you for worlds. Now I mean to see if I can do anything to put matters right, so if you don't mind I'll get going. First I'll call on Chris Dobson and have a talk to her and her mother. Everyone concerned ought to learn a lesson, as I've done, about what harm careless talk can do. Then I'll go on the bus to Mrs. Robinson and try to make her understand how wrong we've both been. Maybe she's thoughtless, as I've been. I don't know how many people she's told, but I'll try to find out and run them all to earth. I shan't forget to call on Jim Atkins—I know him all right. He won't agree to say no more for Christian reasons, but I could give him a warning about the laws of slander.'

'Be careful, Eileen,' Brenda said, but she couldn't refrain from a little smile at this last remark. She got up to see her off and as they reached the door Eileen said,

'Please pray for me—I so want to undo some of the harm I've done—not on my own account, but for Mrs. Peters' sake, and because of what they mentioned about God's name suffering because of me.'

'Cheer up,' Brenda said, 'I know you're right to see what you've done in a serious light, but you know I'm afraid we're all guilty of the same kind of thing quite often. Perhaps if we came to hear of the harm our talking had done, as you have tonight, we'd think more often before we opened our mouths.'

When she got back to the drawing-room the rest of the group were talking.

'I can't see that she'll do much good,' Dennis was saying.

'But at least she's making an effort to put right the wrong she's done,' Brenda said, flying to Eileen's defence, 'and that's important, isn't it?'

'Yes', Jack agreed, 'repentance should be more than a matter of saying sorry to God and the person we've wronged. Wherever possible we should show that we've had a change of heart by taking positive action to put things right. I sometimes think that Christians go in for an awful lot of talking and not much doing.'

'The poor girl didn't mean to hurt us,' Mrs. Peters said. 'If we'd wanted the matter kept completely secret, I shouldn't have come and talked to all of you in the first place. Not that such things don't usually get about in the end.'

'Mainly because of people like Mrs. Robinson,' Sheila said. 'People like that are a menace and in a church they're a disgrace.'

'But if we're honest, we have to admit that we're all inclined to pass on things about people—often not nice things,' Brenda said.

'You're right,' Sheila agreed, 'and often the story grows in the telling. We can give a slightly more exaggerated version not just by embroidering it, but by our tone of voice, or even by the bits of the story we leave out. It seems to be human nature to enjoy telling what we'd call a juicy story. And yet, it's a pretty rotten thing to do.'

'I wonder if people tell themselves, like Eileen did, that they're only passing news on so that another Christian can pray, when, at bottom, it's love of gossip,' Dennis suggested.

'None of us had better throw stones,' Mrs. Peters said, 'not if we know our own hearts. I think Eileen will soon be arriving at Christine's house, so perhaps we could have a time of prayer for her.'

'Yes,' Mr. Peters agreed, 'we bear no bitterness towards any concerned, and if all our hearts are right God can bring some good even out of all this evil.'

SOME QUESTIONS TO THINK ABOUT

Am I a trustworthy friend?
How far have I the right to impose silence on someone to whom I tell confidential matters?
Do I talk about other people's good points, or their bad?
Do I gossip? (Whatever else *I* may call it.)
Am I ready to forgive a wrong done to me?

VERSES TO HELP

You shall not go up and down as a slanderer among your people (Lev. 19. 16, RSV).
Speak evil of no one (Titus 3. 2, RSV).
Let there be . . . no more slander and no more malicious remarks (Eph. 4. 31, Phillips).

The words of a talebearer are as wounds (Prov. 18. 8, and 26. 22, AV).

Things which the Lord hates . . . a false witness who breathes out lies, and a man who sows discord among brothers (Prov. 6. 16, 19, RSV).

Go and do something to show that your hearts are really changed (Matt. 3. 8, Phillips).

Be kind to each other, be understanding. Be as ready to forgive others as God for Christ's sake has forgiven you (Eph. 4. 32, Phillips).

Love . . . does not keep account of evil or gloat over the wickedness of other people. On the contrary, it is glad with all good men when truth prevails (1 Cor. 13. 5b, 6, Phillips).

Chapter 9

'SHE'S DONE NOTHING TO DESERVE CANCER'

'I'M terribly worried about Jean Burrows in our office,' Eileen began, one Thursday evening.

'Not more of your friends having trouble,' Dennis said, amused.

'It's not funny, Dennis, it's awful for her and I don't know what to do. We've had our ups and downs at home, like everyone else, but never real tragedy like this, and I haven't a clue what to say to her.'

'Do you want to talk about it tonight?' Jack asked.

'Yes, I do. I felt a dead loss yesterday, because she came and told me the whole story and I couldn't think of a single thing to say. And she seems to blame God for it.'

'What's happened to her then?' Sheila asked.

'I'd better tell you a bit about her first. Jean's eighteen and the eldest of a large family—five or six of them, I think. We always had that in common—being one of a crowd, I mean—and compared notes on the problems it brings. Her father is more off work than not. She told me once that he'd had an accident when he was a young man, down the mines, and he's never been really fit since. He gets bronchitis almost all the time and, of course, when he's sick there's not that much money to spare. Jean's mum seems a real dear, and she and Jean get on fine. Jean told me a while back that her mum wasn't well but wouldn't go to the doctor—kept saying that one invalid in the family was enough. Well, it seems Jean made her go at last, and they wanted her in hospital straightaway. Jean got worried and had a talk to their doctor, and in the end he told her that it was cancer and very far advanced. He says she won't live long, even though they operate. Jean says if only she'd made her see a doctor earlier she could have been cured, and she's started blaming herself. But mostly she's in a state about the unfairness of it all to her mum. If it was me I think I'd be worrying about who'd look after my dad or the kids, but all Jean kept saying was "Why should a God of love allow a thing like this to happen to my Mum?" The awful thing is that I almost agreed with her—I couldn't think of the right Christian answer.'

'That's not surprising, really,' Jack said; 'it's been

a problem to thousands down the ages.'

'Well, yes, it's always been a worry to me,' Eileen agreed; 'something I ought to try to solve, like a problem in arithmetic that won't work out. But now, suddenly, because of Jean, it's become real and important, like one of those obstacles in a race that you've got to get over before you can go on to the next stage. I feel I've got to find an answer.'

'We know that nothing evil comes from God,' Brenda said, 'the Bible teaches that. So He doesn't send sickness or suffering, does He?'

'But He lets it happen,' Eileen argued. 'We believe God's in charge of the world, so if He doesn't do something to stop suffering, it comes to the same thing as if He sent it, the way most people understand.'

'The fact that He gave mankind free-will means that He has to allow us to make our own choices, and naturally we must put up with the results,' Dennis said. 'You can't give a person the chance to run his own life and then start interfering the whole time to prevent what's bound to follow. It's a matter of cause and effect.'

'But Mrs. Burrows hasn't brought this illness on herself,' Eileen persisted. 'If she'd been taking drugs or drinking, or done something else that had caused it, I suppose you could say she was responsible, but she's done nothing to deserve cancer.'

'It's not always a matter of every individual paying the price of his own sin or self-indulgence,' Sheila explained. 'In road accidents it's often a driver who is selfish or rude who causes the death of another person, and gets away without a scratch himself. Or a factory worker might be careless over fitting a screw in an aircraft, and because of that the crew and passengers could all be killed. We're so closely bound together in life that everything we do affects other people, and the innocent often suffer instead of the guilty.'

'I agree with all that,' Eileen said, 'but I still don't think it helps with my problem. There's no one responsible for what's happened to Mrs. Burrows.'

'Perhaps we just have to accept illness and death as part of the world we live in,' Brenda suggested, 'after all, it's one of the results of the Fall.'

'Yes,' Dennis agreed, 'man disobeying God really threw the whole system out of gear. Nothing on our planet runs smoothly now because the whole balance of nature is upset. Sometimes the actual person who sins has to suffer as a result, but more often than not there's no person directly responsible for illness or sorrow. We're all just reaping the effects of God's perfect creation having been mucked up by man.'

'A fat lot of comfort all that would be to Jean Burrows,' Eileen remarked. 'She kept saying that her mother had always been so good and spent her life thinking of others, and why should this happen to her. If I turned round and said it was just too bad, but the world being the way it was some people had to suffer, she'd probably slap me across the face, and I'd deserve it.'

'Just because you don't offer your theory to some-one when they're in trouble doesn't mean you shouldn't work out the reasons for yourself,' Dennis said. 'You need to sort these matters out before trouble comes to you personally. You're too involved to think about it properly then.'

'I've often heard people talk the way your friend

Jean is doing,' Brenda said. 'They seem to feel that if a person has lived a good life they ought somehow to be shielded from suffering. I've never noticed any connection between the kind of life you lead and the number of troubles you have. If anything, the better people seem to come off worse.'

'What it boils down to is that people believe that God uses suffering as a kind of punishment, and therefore they expect people they think of as good to come off scot free,' Dennis said.

'Do you mean the way Job's friends decided he must have done something wrong to be having so much trouble?' Eileen asked.

'That was certainly their view, and it's an interpretation of suffering that's as old as the hills and which the Bible shows is quite untrue,' Jack replied. 'But I don't think folk believe in the punishment idea so much today. It's more that they feel that good-living people should be let off too much trouble.'

'It's still the same basic idea,' Dennis reasoned, 'belief in a God who awards punishment or prizes in terms of good or bad luck in this life. I agree with Brenda, though. There isn't a shred of evidence in life to support their view—yet so many people hang on to it for some reason.'

'Well, *is* there any explanation we can give?' Eileen asked. 'Why *does* God allow suffering?'

'I don't believe there is any full answer to that question,' Jack said, 'nothing that we can understand in this life. But there is something that we can be very sure about, and that is that God loves every person He has made.'

'The biggest proof of God's love is that He gave His Son to die for us,' Mr. Peters added.

'Yes,' Mrs. Peters agreed, 'if the Lord could come right into the midst of all our trouble and suffering and go through such awful pain and agony Himself, just because He loved us, then we can be sure He doesn't make us suffer out of hardness or not caring. We may not understand His purposes, but we can be sure that they are all in His plan of love for us.'

'How could that be true?' Eileen asked; 'how can God send us unhappiness if He truly loves us?'

'I think God always wants to use pain or trouble to bring us to know Him,' Jack suggested. Lots of folk who don't bother to think of God in the good times begin to look for Him when things go wrong. They may become bitter and turn their backs on Him, but the suffering does open up a path back to God, if they'll only take it.'

'I'd like to help Jean believe that God loves her,' Eileen said, 'but I'm not sure how to set about it.'

'There are many verses you could quote,' Mr. Peters suggested, 'John 3. 16, for a start.'

'But is it any good trotting out texts?' Eileen said.

'Not if we do it in a slick kind of way, as if we've got an easy answer to all their problems,' Jack said.

'No, we must show real love and compassion ourselves if the things we say about God's love are going to mean anything to them,' Mrs. Peters explained. 'I often think the Lord must have had tears in His eyes when He listened to some of the poor troubled souls who came to Him. It says in the Gospels that He had compassion on them, and that kind of sympathy shows in the face. If we listen with patience and love to people pouring out their hearts, it's one way of showing love to them, and it does help to heal and comfort.'

'You mean they'll only believe us talking about a God of love if we show them love ourselves?' Eileen asked.

'I'm sure that's true,' Sheila said, 'and as well as having a loving attitude we should show our love in a practical way. I don't mean visiting with a bunch of grapes, but finding really positive ways of sharing their load. Sometimes a relative needs taking to and from hospital for visiting, or babies need minding. That sort of love often costs us a lot, but it really tells people something about God's love.'

'I'm not sure that it's a good thing to *say* "I'll pray for you" to someone in trouble,' Dennis said, 'but I am sure that it's terribly important that we *do* pray regularly and sincerely for our friends when they're having a rough time.'

'I know,' Eileen agreed, 'and I remember to pray when I'm really worked up about their troubles as I am over Jean now. But it's hard to keep it up and really mean it. I want to keep praying for Jean, though, and I want to think how I can help her by looking after the younger kids sometimes, or something like that. Perhaps it's best if I don't try to talk to her about God too much yet. I'll wait till it seems the right time and I have the right thing to say.'

'Trouble comes to us all at some time,' Mrs. Peters said, 'and that's when knowing the Lord makes such a difference. Sometimes we need God's chastening— a bit of trouble is good for our characters and it beings us back to leaning on the Lord, often after we've been trying to go in our own strength. But what I've found most of all is that having had some trouble yourself makes you more understanding and sympathetic with others in the same state. Those who've had an easy path in life can often be cold and even harsh in what they say to those in need. If we've been through sorrow ourselves we can enter into how they're feeling, and we can often pass on to them some little bit of comfort that the Lord's given to us.'

'I wish I had your experience, Mrs. Peters, so that I knew what to say.'

'Wait a bit—is it the Burrows in Larkspur Road?' Mr. Peters asked.

'Yes,' Eileen said.

'Then you do know them, Mother, they're often in the shop. You could call in on Mrs. Burrows yourself, couldn't you?' Mr. Peters suggested.

'That would be lovely,' Eileen said, 'and if everyone here prays for them and we do what we can to help, Mrs. Peters, perhaps the whole family may find there's something good to be learned from all this trouble.'

QUESTIONS TO THINK ABOUT

Do I show true compassion towards friends and neighbours facing trouble?

Do I use my own pain and sorrow to understand and help those in need?

Do I pray consistently for them?

Am I ready to listen sympathetically, or do I only want to give advice?

Do I show that God loves them by my own actions towards them?

SOME VERSES TO HELP

He who did not grudge His own Son but gave Him

up for us all—can we not trust such a God to give us, with Him, everything else we can need? (Rom. 8. 32, Phillips).

Share . . . the sorrow of those who are sad (Rom. 12. 15, Phillips).

If a fellow man or woman has no clothes to wear and nothing to eat, and one of you say, "Good luck to you, I hope you'll keep warm and find enough to eat," and yet give them nothing to meet their physical needs, what on earth is the good of that? (James 2. 15, 16, Phillips).

Thank God, the Father of our Lord Jesus Christ, that He is our Father and the source of all mercy and comfort. For He gives us comfort in our trials so that we in turn may be able to give the same sort of strong sympathy to others in theirs (2 Cor. 1. 3, 4, Phillips).

Chapter 10

NO EASY ANSWERS

'I'M sorry this will be the last time we meet till the Autumn,' Sheila began; 'I've really enjoyed these discussions.'

'I was wondering how everyone felt about them,' Jack said, 'and I thought we could sum things up a bit this evening. Does everyone feel they've been helpful?'

There were nods and sounds of assent. Then Eileen said,

'Yes and no. I mean that I've enjoyed talking over all these problems, and yet I'm a bit disappointed because I don't feel I've got all the answers. I started off keeping a notebook, and when I got home I used to jot down the question we'd been dealing with, hoping that I could fill in the right answer at the bottom of the page. Looking through now, I find I've hardly got any answers, but a whole lot of "ifs" and "it all depends". I don't think it's a bit satisfactory.'

'But there *are* no easy answers,' Sheila insisted. 'You can't expect to have everything neatly labelled and pigeon-holed, unless you grossly over-simplify life.'

'I sometimes think we were happier in the old days,' Mrs. Peters said. 'When we were young we were given a strict set of rules, with "do's" and "don't's" for every subject. I think they kept us on the right path.'

'Too few rules today,' Mr. Peters agreed; 'young people are allowed to do what they like—attend any places of amusement, go in for all the fashions—and look at the result.'

'Young people today mature much sooner,' Dennis said. 'A set of rules that a child would accept won't suit them. Trying to treat them like that just wouldn't work.'

'And life today is much more complicated,' Jack said. 'A generation ago it was easier to keep things separate in different watertight compartments. People could refuse to go to the theatre, the cinema or the races, for example, whereas today television brings these things into our homes. If we try to cut ourselves off from the mass media of television, radio, the newspapers and so on, we'll merely succeed in being eccentric and out of touch with our neighbours and their needs.'

'Yet somehow we've got to bear a clear Christian witness in the midst of belonging to our own age,' Sheila added.

'And right is still right, and wrong still wrong,' Mr. Peters said. 'That's what has been forgotten.'

'If we get back to the subjects we've been discussing during the past months,' Dennis suggested, 'we shall find they've not involved questions where the Bible gives an open-and-shut case for or against.'

'Except where we talked about gossip,' Eileen reminded him. 'I got a quick answer to fill in at the bottom of that page.'

'But in most cases we had to agree that a great deal depends on the individual people and circumstances concerned. For example, you can't give a short answer to the problem of coping with middle-age or marriage.'

'It's a pity all the same,' Eileen complained. 'I'd

like to have these things sorted out for me once for all.'

'That's because you're lazy,' Dennis said.

'No, I don't think it's that,' Brenda protested. 'If Eileen's like me, she's afraid of making mistakes. If we have a foolproof answer to a problem we aren't worried about doing the wrong thing.'

Eileen nodded in agreement.

'No one ever said anything about the Christian life being straightforward and easy,' Dennis said severely. 'We've got to have a sense of adventure and be on our toes the whole time. It's no good wanting to play dead safe.'

'God does us the courtesy of treating us as individuals,' Sheila said, 'but that privilege brings with it the responsibility of acting according to our own conscience, and not someone else's.'

'I'm not sure that I can trust my conscience to come up with the right answer,' Eileen said doubtfully.

'The Scriptures lay down principles for us to follow,' Mr. Peters reminded her.

'But life is so different today from when the Bible was written,' Eileen protested.

'Yet human nature is very much the same,' Jack said, 'and God never changes. The problems we have may not appear in their present form within the pages of the Bible, but the kind of attitude we should have to other people, to material things, to God Himself—all these are perfectly clear.'

'Every generation has to work these principles out afresh,' Dennis said, 'in terms of their own circumstances. We can't afford to take over second-hand ideas from a previous generation. They won't fit us, anyway, any more than their clothes and fashions would.'

'Life is changing at a much greater rate nowadays,' Sheila continued, 'and if we stay in the same old rut and stop thinking, the Church will cease to be of any help to men and women looking for the truth. We have too much of a reputation already for being out of date and out of touch with life.'

'That's why I feel so strongly about teaching the kids at the Youth Club to think for themselves,' Dennis went on. 'I don't want them to take over my views, but to learn to sort things for themselves.'

'Wait a minute,' Eileen said; 'that may sound good, but I think it means you're shirking your responsibilities. I know teenagers seem very sure of themselves these days, but I think a lot of them are looking for a bit of help and advice from us older ones. They don't want the law laid down—as in the old days—but they do want to know what they ought to do—a lot of them, anyway. I think you should tell them what's right and wrong—things like the ten commandments, I mean, in the sort of words they understand. It's not going to be any help if you just tell them to go away and think out their own views. It's a bit like leaving them to drown.'

'I hope I do tell them pretty clearly where it's a matter of right and wrong,' Dennis replied, 'and I always give my advice pretty straight from the shoulder when they ask for it. But I want them to understand why I have these standards and why I think the way I do, so that they can see the point behind it all. If they're going to do this, they've got to think for themselves.'

'*We* have to go on thinking for ourselves, too,'

Jack said. 'I always imagined, when I was young, that I would have solved most of the problems of life by the time I was forty. I hadn't, of course, and even some of the things I thought I knew the answers to have had to be thought out all over again because of some new experience or a bit more understanding of God's Word.'

'But, as I said, it's difficult sometimes to apply the Bible to your problems,' Eileen objected.

'Remember that we can ask for God's help and guidance,' Mrs. Peters suggested, 'and that we have His promise of the Holy Spirit to lead us into truth, if we are really willing to obey what He shows us in His Word.'

'Aren't I allowed to ask other human beings at all?' Eileen asked.

'Of course,' Dennis said, 'else why have discussions as we've done? We learn a lot by comparing notes and sharing each other's experiences. But, in the end, we must act on our own initiative, not because anyone else tells us to.'

'I'm glad you used the word "act",' Jack said; 'as I said once before, I think, it's only too easy to spend our time talking and forget that action is the whole purpose of the exercise.'

'Yes,' Mr. Peters agreed, 'they say that fine words butter no parsnips, and a lot of discussion won't do any good unless we find what God wants us to do, and do it.'

'I think it might be a good scheme if we all made a list of the subjects we discussed, as Eileen has, and some of the answers we discovered, and then noted down what action we've taken in each case. That will be the best test of all as to whether our discussions have really been worthwhile,' Jack concluded. Every-one agreed.

SOME QUESTIONS TO THINK ABOUT

Do I differentiate between clear matters of right and wrong and those where individual Christian opinion may vary?

Do I rely on second-hand views and easy rules to tell me what to do?

Am I always ready to think out my own beliefs after prayerful study of the Bible?

Do I help others and myself by sharing views and experiences with fellow-Christians?

Does my talking have an outlet in action?

SOME VERSES TO HELP

All Scripture is inspired by God and is useful for teaching the faith and correcting error, for re-setting the direction of a man's life and training him in good living. The Scriptures are the comprehensive equip-ment of the man of God, and fit him fully for all branches of his work (2 Tim. 3. 16, 17, Phillips).

If you have a clear conviction, apply it to yourself in the sight of God. Happy is the man who can make his decision with a clear conscience (Rom. 14. 22, NEB).

Not everyone who says to Me, 'Lord, Lord,' shall enter the Kingdom of Heaven, but he who does the will of My Father who is in Heaven (Matt. 7. 21, RSV).

Work out your own salvation with fear and trem-bling; for God is at work in you, both to will and to work for His good pleasure (Phil. 2. 12b, 13, RSV).

When that one I have spoken to you about comes—the Spirit of truth—He will guide you into everything that is true (John 16. 13, Phillips).